"Who are you?" Lauren asked.

Joe dropped the lightest of kisses on her forehead. "Ask me again sometime," he murmured. "Try to go back to sleep. We'll talk more tomorrow."

He tucked her in as tenderly as he would a child, but something in his face told her he didn't think of her as a child at all. "Good night, Lauren."

"Good night," she whispered.

He left her wishing he would sleep beside her again, and angry with herself for even acknowledging feelings she shouldn't have, couldn't trust. Her whole world was turned upside down, she thought wearily. She was too vulnerable, too frightened, to know how to interpret her feelings—or his actions. She had to keep remembering that.

But it was the feel of Joe's arms around her, his lips brushing her forehead, that lingered with her as she closed her eyes and drifted back to sleep.

Dear Reader:

Romance readers have been enthusiastic about the Silhouette Special Editions for years. And that's not by accident: Special Editions were the first of their kind and continue to feature realistic stories with heightened romantic tension.

The longer stories, sophisticated style, greater sensual detail and variety that made Special Editions popular are the same elements that will make you want to read book after book.

We hope that you enjoy this Special Edition today, and will enjoy many more.

Please write to us:

Jane Nicholls
Silhouette Books
PO Box 236
Thornton Road
Croydon
Surrey
CR9 3RU

GINA FERRIS
Far to Go

Silhouette Special Edition

Originally Published by Silhouette Books
a division of
Harlequin Enterprises Ltd.

*First published in Great Britain in 1994
by Silhouette Books, Eton House, 18-24 Paradise Road,
Richmond, Surrey TW9 1SR*

© Gina Wilkins 1994

*Silhouette, Silhouette Special Edition and Colophon are
Trade Marks of Harlequin Enterprises B.V.*

ISBN 0 373 59242 6

23-9406

Made and printed in Great Britain

GINA FERRIS

declares that she is Southern by birth and by choice, and she has chosen to set many of her books in the South, where she finds a rich treasury of characters and settings. She particularly loves the Ozark mountain region of northern Arkansas and southern Missouri, and the proudly unique people who reside there. She and her husband, John, live in Jacksonville, Arkansas, with their three children, Courtney, Kerry and David.

Other Silhouette Books by Gina Ferris

Silhouette Special Edition

Healing Sympathy
Lady Beware
In From the Rain
Prodigal Father
*Full of Grace
*Hardworking Man
*Fair and Wise

Family Found

Monday's child is fair of face.
Tuesday's child is full of grace.
Wednesday's child is full of woe.
Thursday's child has far to go.
Friday's child is loving and giving.
Saturday's child works hard for its living.
But the child that is born on the Sabbath Day
is fair and wise and good and gay.

—Anon.

Prologue

Private investigator Tony D'Alessandro looked up from his paper-covered desk when the door to his office opened. "Jared. Come in," he greeted his brother-in-law. "Have a seat."

The deeply tanned cowboy in worn denims and scuffed boots draped himself in the chair beside the desk. "What's up? Why'd you want me to drop by while I was in town today? Does it have anything to do with the twins?"

"Yeah," Tony admitted, pushing aside a precariously balanced mountain of paperwork. "Man, I'm swamped," he muttered. "I've been shorthanded ever since I had to fire Bob last year. Neither of the two replacements I hired for him have worked out."

"Guess it didn't help that Cassie quit when she did," Jared said with a touch of apology in his gravelly voice.

Tony shrugged good naturedly. "I don't blame her for wanting to take the time to prepare for the baby. Helping with the ranch as well as taking care of you and Shane and setting up a nursery is more than enough for her to tackle."

"It doesn't help that she's so sleepy all the time," Jared agreed with a chuckle. "She nods off at the damndest times. Her doctor says it's perfectly normal, but it could be a problem if she were on a case for you."

"I can see where it would be."

"How about Michelle? She feeling okay?"

The mention of his wife—Jared's sister—made Tony smile, as always. "She's fine. She's never been happier than since she learned we're expecting."

"Good for her." Jared's own smile faded as he grew abruptly serious. "Okay, Tony, let's have it. What have you found on the twins?"

Tony sighed and ran a hand through his ebony hair. "To tell you the truth, it's getting weird. The few leads I've had have ended so abruptly, it's like slamming into a brick wall. Something just doesn't feel right about this."

"They've been missing almost fifteen years, since they ran away from their last foster home when they were sixteen," Jared pointed out logically. "You reunited the rest of us almost too easily. I suppose we should have expected that we wouldn't find the twins as quickly as we did the others."

"That's just it, Jared. I've found a few clues, but each time I think I'm getting somewhere, I end up having doors slammed in my face. It's almost as though..."

"As though?"

"As though they're getting assistance in keeping their whereabouts secret. Major assistance."

Jared looked at his brother-in-law with open skepticism. "Cloak-and-dagger stuff? Doesn't seem likely."

Tony sighed. "I know. I'm probably just being paranoid. Hell, I don't even have proof that the twins are still alive. This has simply been the most frustrating case I've ever been involved with.''

''Maybe because it's personal this time,'' Jared suggested. ''Your client is your wife. You know how badly she wants to find her last two siblings. You're putting too much pressure on yourself to please her, especially now that she's pregnant.''

Tony considered the words for a moment, then lifted a shoulder. ''Maybe you're right. I *do* want to find the twins —for Michelle, and for the rest of you. But I still think there's something strange going on in their case. I just wish I had more manpower to help out right now.''

''I realize that good investigators aren't exactly lined up at every employment office.''

''Tell me about it. I'm about to get desperate enough to beg my father to come out of retirement and go back to work for me—or vice versa.''

Jared chuckled. ''Can't see Vinnie leaving his gardening to go back on stakeouts.''

''No,'' Tony agreed reluctantly. ''Neither can I.''

''You haven't given up on finding Joey and Bobby, have you?'' Jared asked quietly, his smile fading.

Tony's jaw hardened. ''No. No matter how long it takes, or how many strings I have to pull, I'm not giving up. Your brothers are out there somewhere, Jared. And I'm going to find them.''

Chapter One

"Damn it, where is she?"

"I thought she went this way."

"I don't see her. What if she fell into the stream?"

"Then she's dead. Even if she lived through the fall from that bluff, those floodwaters would take her under in seconds. No one could swim in those currents."

"You're probably right. Still—"

"Ah, the hell with it. This storm's getting worse and the roads down this godforsaken mountain are almost impassable now. Let's get out of here!"

"But the woman—"

"We'll come back when the storm's over. We found her once, we can find her again."

"Yeah, guess you're right. Okay, let's get out of this damned storm. Looks like all hell's about to break loose. I don't want..."

The distorted, shouting voices faded away, leaving no sound in Lauren's living nightmare but the torrents of rain pounding down on her battered body, and the roar of the furiously rising, flooding stream, which was already pulling at her bleeding legs. Only semiconscious, she was unable to move for the moment, paralyzed by fear and pain. She was afraid they were still up there, the two men who had hurt her, who had tried to kidnap her. Even now they could be standing on the embankment twenty feet above her; the very embankment from which she had just fallen in her desperate escape from them.

The tumble down had been long and agonizing, jagged rocks and twisted tree limbs tearing at skin already bruised from the beating she had received. If she hadn't caught hold of a small, little-more-than-bush-size tree on the stream bank with her right hand, she'd have been carried downstream by now with all the other debris being swept along in the roiling, swelling waters.

The pain. Oh, God, the pain. Like nothing she'd ever known. Like nothing...

No. She could not drift off. The roar of the stream was getting louder, angrier, by the moment as the rain continued to swell its banks. The water covered her legs, reaching ever higher to pull her into the rapids. She was already so wet from the rain that it was hard to tell how much of her body was under water.

It would be so easy to close her eyes, close her mind, and let the water wash away this pain...

No! She wouldn't let them win. Damn them to hell, they wouldn't get away with this! All her life she'd had to fight for what she wanted and now she wanted to live.

She lifted her head out of the sucking mud, the movement almost driving her into unconsciousness. Struggling for breath, she opened her eyes and tried to focus, but rain and darkness were all she could see. Even if she had the strength to scream, she doubted that there would be anyone in these woods at this hour of the night to hear. No one except her would-be killers. She decided not to waste the effort.

Her left arm was twisted beneath her, useless. With her right arm, she pulled experimentally against the tree, trying to lift herself higher on the bank. She didn't move. Filling her lungs with cold, rain-soaked air, she struggled for a foothold, but the water kept pulling at her legs, forcing them upward and sideways. Her shoes were gone, lost somewhere during the terrified run from the mountain cabin in which she'd been staying on this supposedly peaceful, solitary vacation. So much for peace and rest, she thought hazily, searching again with her toes.

There! A rock. She curled the toes of her right foot, pushing against it with all her strength, to no avail. Clinging to the tree, she stopped briefly to recoup, resting her forehead on her outstretched arm. She was crying, her ragged sobs inaudible even to her beneath the din of the storm. But the creeping waters were almost to her waist and she couldn't afford to wait any longer.

The tree bent against her weight, its delicate trunk proving little contest against the powerful flooding stream. A frustrated cry escaped her as she pulled again without noticeable effect. Her feet thrashed in the water, pushing and digging for a hold.

She whimpered a little sound of relief when she felt her body slowly responding to her efforts. Gasping, trembling, crying, straining, she dragged herself another couple of inches higher, her injured left arm hindering her forward slide. And then the tree released its tenuous hold on the melting earth anchoring it, pulling up roots and all in Lauren's white-knuckled fist.

She screamed in rage and despair as her body slid back down toward the hungry water. Her cry rose in unearthly echo above the storm's roar.

Scrabbling with her feet and one good arm for rocks, roots, anything to save her, she almost didn't notice the wildly swinging beam of a powerful flashlight that flickered across her, froze, then returned. But she heard the voice—the deep, wonderful voice bellowing down from above. "Hang on, lady! Don't let go, I'm on my way."

She tried, but there was nothing to hang on to. Her clutching fingers dug long, water-filled furrows in the mud as the stream lifted her, preparing to run with her, its mad bellow sounding mockingly victorious to her weary ears.

And then strong fingers closed around her wrist and her shoulder was nearly pulled from its socket with a tug that jerked her upward, partially out of the water. "Help me, lady!" the man yelled. "Give me your other hand."

"I can't!" she shouted back. "I think it's broken."

A string of grunted curses came from her rescuer, who was struggling to keep his footing in the slimy mud, fighting the stream for its hostage. One almost superhuman yank brought her fully out of the water. She screamed at the pain. The man lost his balance and fell backward, tumbling her on top of him.

"We've got to get out of here," he shouted. "The stream is still rising. Can you walk?"

When she didn't immediately answer, he shook her roughly. "Hey! Can you hear me?"

Her head lolling weakly, she struggled to stay conscious. "Y-yes," she answered finally, hoping he could hear her. She had no strength left to shout.

"All right. Hang on, now. Don't faint yet. You've got to help me just a little longer." He pushed himself to his feet, dragging her with him.

The excruciatingly slow journey up the embankment was almost as unendurable as her tumbling descent had been. She doubted that she'd ever remember the details, only the pain and the man's hard strength as he half carried, half pulled her to safety. She knew when they reached the top by his moan of relief, and then she was unable to hold on any longer. Her fall was broken by her rescuer's quick reaction. Even as she lost the battle to stay alert, she felt him swing her high in his arms, against a chest that seemed broad and strong enough to defeat even nature gone mad.

A jostling movement and the pain that followed woke her. Dazed and disoriented, she found herself locked into a pair of strong arms, being carried through the storm, the face above her obscured by rain and darkness. Instinctively, she began to struggle as memories crashed down on her. "No! Let me go! I won't let you—"

The man stumbled when her frantic movements threw him off-balance, though he recovered quickly. "Damn it, lady," the familiar voice growled in her ear. "Will you be still? I'm trying to help you."

"Oh," she murmured, subsiding against his broad chest again, remembering the man who'd pulled her out of the stream. "It's you. I thought you were one of them."

"The name's Joe," he told her over the noise of the storm. "Hold on now, we're almost to my cabin."

She started to shiver, so forcefully that she had to cling to him with her good right hand to steady herself in his arms. "I'm cold," she whispered through stiff lips.

His arms tightened comfortingly. "Yeah. Me, too. Just hang in there another few minutes, okay?"

"I'll try," she whispered in response, resting her head against his shoulder again. She tried to hold on to consciousness, but it was so easy to let the pain and fear slip away, knowing this man—this stranger—was taking care of her.

She closed her eyes.

It was dry in his cabin, and quieter than outside in the fury of the storm. It was probably warm, as well, but Lauren was so cold and wet and frightened that the warmth couldn't penetrate her icy skin. The violent shivers roused her again, a thin gasp of pain leaving her trembling lips. She was lying on a bed, her wet, matted head resting on a pillow. The room was dark, the man leaning over her only a darker shape against the shadows. His hands fumbled with her sodden clothing and she slapped ineffectively against them. "What are you doing?" she demanded, her voice little more than a croak.

"I've got to get you out of these wet things," he said, easily overpowering her feeble resistance as he tugged her shorts down her hips. He tossed the garment aside. He reached for the buttons of her blouse, efficiently, expertly releasing them.

Lauren's cheeks flamed as he carefully eased the garment down her throbbing left arm, and she was glad the room was dark. Her rescuer—Joe, he'd called himself—wasn't. "Damn this storm," he muttered beneath his breath. "Electricity's out. I can't see how badly you're hurt. As soon as I get you wrapped in something warm, I'll light a lantern."

The blanket was blissfully warm and soft. Lauren snuggled into it, moaning quietly at the assorted pains that radiated through her body. Her head, her face, her arm, her legs—everywhere. Eyes closed, she heard rustling noises from somewhere else in the room. Joe must be changing his own wet clothes, she thought, trying to concentrate on anything but the pain. And the fear.

Were they still out there, looking for her?

Who was Joe, and how had he happened upon her, out in the woods, at midnight, during a raging storm?

Was he . . . ? *Oh, God, was he one of them?*

She jerked her head upward at the horrifying possibility. The resulting explosion of pain made her cry out and reach up with both hands to press against her temples. Every nerve in her injured left arm screamed at the movement, and darkness overtook her again. The last thing she heard was Joe's startled curse, his hands touching her just as she lost consciousness.

Joe had never felt more helpless and frustrated than he did as he crouched over the woman lying on his bed. Beneath the mud, blood and bruises, her face was pale in the harsh glare of the lantern—so pale, and still he found himself watching her chest rise and fall just to reassure himself she was still breathing.

With a warm, soapy washcloth, he wiped away as much mud as he could, trying to take inventory of her injuries. There was a fairly deep cut on her forehead, still oozing blood, and a sizable lump beneath it. He'd bet his next paycheck she had a concussion. The right side of her face was covered by a swelling, darkening bruise. She could have gotten it during her fall—but it looked to him as though someone had hit her. Hard.

His muttered imprecations echoed in the dark corners of the room. His curses were aimed at the men who'd attacked her, at her father for doing so little to protect her—and at himself, for almost being too late to save her.

She needed to be in a hospital. He was no doctor, had no way of knowing how bad her injuries really were. She moaned softly when he carefully straightened her swollen left arm, though she didn't awaken. He thought it was only sprained, not broken, but what if he was wrong? What if there were internal injuries in addition to the concussion he suspected?

A flash of lightning brightened the corners of the room for a moment, then vanished to plunge them back into shadows. A moment later a crash of thunder rattled the windows and made the woman stir restlessly in her sleep. Rain pounded against the roof, driven by wind that howled like a hungry animal in the night. And somewhere out there, people were looking for Lauren Caldwell, people who must not be allowed to find her.

Taking her to a hospital was not an option—at least not now. The roads were nearly impassable in the storm, even with his four-wheel drive. He'd probably kill her trying to get her there. And if he didn't, someone else might once she was discovered there. All in all, she was safer where she was at the moment.

She made a quiet, whimpering sound in her sleep and his chest tightened. Looked as if it was up to him to help her as best he could. She needed him.

He only hoped he'd do a better job of taking care of her now than he had earlier that evening.

The attackers were back. The big one, the one who had hurt her so brutally, was so close she could feel his hot breath on her skin. He was going to kill her.

"No!" she choked, throwing her arms up to ward him off. And then she cried out as burning spears of pain pierced her left arm. She called to the man who had saved her before, praying he would be there for her again. "Joe, stop him! Please don't let him—"

"I'm here" came the wonderful voice in her ear. "You're safe."

She turned her face into his broad shoulder. "I'm sorry. I don't know what's wrong with me."

"It's all right, Lauren. It was just a dream."

"I thought—I felt him. His breath was so hot . . ."

"There's no one here but me, and I'm the good guy, okay? You have a fever. That's why you feel so hot."

Hot? She was cold. So cold. She began to tremble, her teeth chattering. "The water," she moaned. "The water was so cold."

"Open your mouth. I want you to take these pills." Something pressed against her lips.

She hesitated.

"Do it for me, okay? It'll help, I promise."

How could she refuse him, when he had saved her life? She opened her mouth and swallowed the pills with an effort, washing them down with the cool water he offered afterward. The room was dark, her swollen eyes so glazed that he was still no more than a silhouette against the shadows. She wished she could see him clearly. She wanted very badly to see him.

"That's good," Joe encouraged her when she'd finally choked down the pills.

Secure in his care, she began to breathe more evenly, her eyelids drooping. "You won't leave me?" she couldn't resist asking. A part of her was appalled that she was being so uncharacteristically dependent on this man who was, after all, a stranger to her. But she couldn't bear the thought of being left alone again.

"I won't leave you. Go to sleep, Lauren."

Lauren drifted off again, knowing Joe was there beside her, guarding against the evils lurking in the shadows.

* * *

She didn't know how long she'd been asleep. It seemed like a long time. Her dreams had been vivid and disturbing, her rest fitful. She lay still, aware that every inch of her body hurt and her head was pounding painfully. A sound penetrated the dull throbbing. Rain. Rain hammering against windowpanes. The memories jolted her, causing her to open her eyes with a gasp.

Her vision was fuzzy, distorted by flashes of light she associated with her vicious headache. Very slowly, she moved her eyes, unwilling to risk the pain of further movement. The room was small, with rough-paneled walls and a bare light bulb, turned off, suspended above her head. It reminded her of the cabin in which she'd been staying for the past week in the secluded Arkansas Ozarks. She lay in an iron-frame bed, a worn blue blanket covering her body. She wore what seemed to be a man's white T-shirt and nothing else.

Startled, she looked around more wildly, seeking the man who'd pulled her out of that stream—when? Was it last night he had found her and brought her here? Had it been longer?

She was alone in the room. Trying to ignore her body's appalled protest, she cautiously tried to sit up, and then almost fell forward when she did. Breaking into a clammy sweat, she fought nausea, the room going gray around her as she swayed toward the edge of the bed.

"Lauren! What the hell are you doing?" The familiar voice scolded her as Joe's strong hands caught her and eased her back down onto the pillow. "You're in no condition to get up."

"I—I wanted to—" Her stomach wrenched. "I think I'm going to be sick!" she gasped.

"Here's a bowl," he answered promptly, putting a hand behind her neck. "I'll help you sit up."

Taking several long, deep breaths, she slowly shook her head. "No. No, it's passed. For now."

"Good." He removed his hand. "You shouldn't have anything left in your stomach."

"Have I . . . have I been sick?" she asked, staring up at him. His face was blurred by the dim lighting and her hazy focusing, but she got an impression of golden brown hair and nicely carved features before she closed her eyes against the shooting lights that flashed before them.

"You don't remember?"

"No."

"You've been sick. You've had a fever and chills and nausea and you've been delirious. Frankly, you had me worried for a while. I've aged at least ten years in the twelve hours since I found you."

The gentle note of humor in his deep voice brought a weak smile to her lips. "Sorry," she murmured drowsily. "God, my head hurts."

"I've brought you some more aspirin." He lifted her head enough so that she could swallow the tablets with a few sips of water. "Try to get some more rest. It's the best thing for you."

"What time is it?"

"Just after noon. No more questions, now. Go back to sleep."

"Yes, Joe. Thank you."

"You're welcome, honey."

The soft endearment slipped around her like a down comforter, warming her as she slipped without resistance into healing, restful sleep.

* * *

"Lauren?" The quiet voice brought her eyes open slowly to narrow in concentration at the man leaning over her. Gold-streaked brown hair, nicely carved features. Joe.

"What is it?" Her voice came out in an unintelligible croak.

"You okay? You were moaning when I woke you."

"I hurt," she admitted frankly. "I've never hurt so badly in my life."

"I don't suppose you have," he responded in sympathy. "But you don't seem to be running a fever now. How many fingers am I holding up?"

She tried to focus. "Four?" she ventured.

He dropped his hand to touch her cheek. "Close enough. You're going to be fine."

She murmured a response through a yawn.

"Go back to sleep, Lauren. I'll check on you again later."

She was asleep before he left the room.

In the cabin's main room, Joe paced, glaring at the radio he'd been talking into, his brows drawn into a scowl. It had been all he could do to hang on to his temper during the confrontation he'd just had with Marcus Caldwell, Lauren's father. Caldwell had blamed Joe for the attack on Lauren, had even implied that he should have found someone else to watch over his daughter. Unfairly, of course.

Joe had said from the beginning that the security measures they'd taken to protect Lauren weren't sufficient, that there should be at least two bodyguards watching over her. That the midnight check-in calls to Chicago had been more dangerous than useful, leaving Lauren alone and vulnerable for some twenty minutes each night, at the worst possible time.

Caldwell had insisted from the beginning that Lauren wasn't really in danger, that the threats against her had been all bluff, that getting her out of Chicago and into a secluded Ozark mountain cabin had been protection enough, Joe's presence hardly necessary. Just a little extra precaution, he'd said.

And now he blamed Joe for his own false confidence.

"Bastard," Joe muttered, shoving a hand through his hair. It was bad enough that Caldwell had all but invited this mess in the first place. Now he seemed intent on making things worse, giving orders and tossing around threats that couldn't possibly help the situation they found themselves in. He'd refused to listen to any of Joe's suggestions, saying he'd get back to him after he'd consulted with his "security experts."

"What does he think *I* am?" Joe grumbled darkly. "A professional baby-sitter?"

At least Caldwell had agreed that Joe had done the right thing by keeping Lauren here, for now, and not rushing her to the nearest hospital. He'd sounded relieved that Joe didn't think Lauren's injuries were life-threatening, though he'd swiftly masked any of the initial emotion that had crept into his voice as he'd asked about his only daughter. And he'd concurred that keeping Lauren safe in a small, rural hospital would be difficult. He'd brusquely ordered Joe to stand by, proceed as he had been, until Caldwell got back to him with further instructions.

Joe only wished he could be absolutely certain that Lauren's health wasn't at risk by keeping her here. He knew she had a concussion, and he'd been watching her closely, waking her at regular intervals, relieved that she'd responded each time. It hadn't reassured him that she'd counted four fingers when he'd held up two. He didn't think there were internal injuries or broken bones, but he was taking a major gamble trying to treat her himself. He hoped his actions were justified by the danger he believed her to be in if they left without a plan of some sort. As long as her attackers thought there was at least a chance that she was dead, she was probably better off where she was.

He hoped.

Joe shoved his hands into the pockets of his jeans, fighting the guilt that swamped him every time he thought of the attack on Lauren Caldwell. He'd been watching over her for the past week, grabbing a couple hours' sleep during the day, never letting her out of his sight for longer than absolutely necessary, but it had been a difficult assignment for only one man. And they'd gotten to her, despite Caldwell's frequent reassurances that the odds were slim that anyone would try.

If Joe could get his hands on the men who'd hit her, who'd chased her through the woods and over that bluff, who'd come so close to causing her to drown in the flooding stream, he'd kill them.

And then he blinked in surprise at the very intensity of the thought. Emotion was something he rarely allowed to interfere with his actions. He was startled by the depth of fury he felt whenever he thought of anyone hurting the small, slender woman now lying in his bed. She'd been beaten, had fallen over a bluff and had been left to die. And still she'd fought—the flooding stream, him, the fever that had racked her during the long night. He admired the spirit it had taken for her to keep fighting.

Lauren Caldwell was quite a woman. Maybe as stubborn as her father.

She wasn't much to look at just now, but he'd been watching her in secret for almost a week and had felt his breath catch in his chest on more than one occasion when he'd been struck by her beauty.

He'd watched her walking slowly, thoughtfully, along the very stream in which she'd come so close to dying, the springtime sun streaming through greening tree branches to glitter in the rich, dark blond hair that fell to the middle of her back. He'd wondered what color her eyes were—now he knew they were a bright green, the same shade as the new spring leaves.

The graceful movements of her slight, feminine body—the same body he'd treated so impersonally during the past hours—had made him shift uncomfortably on more than one occasion in his various hiding places. He'd been attracted to other women, of course, but rarely while he was working—and never so powerfully, or so soon.

He didn't welcome this attraction. Hadn't been at all pleased by the sheer terror that had gripped him when he'd realized her cabin was empty and ransacked, when he'd finally found her lying almost submerged in the flooding stream, only moments from being swept away from him forever. Nor had he known what to think about the unexpected surge of possessive protectiveness he'd felt when he'd held her in his arms as she'd wept in the throes of a feverish nightmare, clinging to him as if he were her one hope of salvation. Feelings like these could be a serious detriment to the job he had to do.

"Damn," he muttered, his eyes focused grimly on the door to the bedroom. "I'm getting too old for this." It was a consideration that had been occurring to him with increasing regularity lately, one he hadn't liked any better than his unprecedented obsession with Lauren Caldwell.

He didn't know what, exactly, he was going to do about either problem.

Chapter Two

Lauren smelled the soup before she was fully aware that she was awake. Her lashes fluttered, then opened. Joe was watching her from the chair beside the bed, his gold-streaked hair gleaming softly in the light from the bare bulb overhead. She smiled, the movement pulling uncomfortably at her bruised, swollen mouth. "Hi," she whispered. "The electricity's back on, I see."

"Has been for hours. Feel any better?"

"My head doesn't hurt as badly. I seem to be focusing better. Other than that . . ." She let her voice trail off, her wince finishing the sentence for her.

"Think you could eat a little chicken soup?"

"Chicken soup?" she repeated weakly. "You wouldn't have your mother hidden in the kitchen, would you?"

Joe smiled. "No. Just a can opener." He rose from his chair and lifted a bowl and spoon from the top of a functional dresser, carrying them to the small nightstand beside the bed. "I'll prop you up on the pillows and then feed you."

"I'm not really very hungry," she commented doubtfully, holding the blanket to her throat with her good hand as she thought of how thin the T-shirt was that she wore. Silly of her to be concerned, of course, since the man had stripped her down to nothing before putting the shirt on her.

"You need to build up your strength," he answered firmly, reaching for her.

She shrank back.

Joe stopped, looking at her with concern. "What's wrong, Lauren? You know I won't hurt you, don't you?"

Swallowing hard, she nodded. "I know. It's just..."

"Reaction," he finished for her, seeming to understand. "I promise not to hurt you, but I really wish you'd try to eat a little. Please," he added with an attractively entreating smile.

She'd already decided that he was a very good-looking man, with his beautifully proportioned features, lazy-lidded, crystal blue eyes and thick, slightly wavy hair. His intriguingly crooked smile made her reaffirm that observation. She was hardly in any condition to ogle a handsome man, but her reaction confirmed that she was alive and getting stronger. She'd have to be dying, at least, not to be affected by that particular smile.

Feeling herself flush beneath her bruises, she released her grip on the sheet. "I'm sorry. Of course you won't hurt me. You've been wonderful. You saved my life."

He grunted a typically masculine response to the praise and slipped a hand beneath her head to lift her gently off the pillows, being especially careful not to jar her left arm, which was propped on other pillows beside her. She looked at the swollen arm, from which radiated waves of discomfort she'd been trying hard to ignore. "Is it broken?"

"I don't think so. It's badly sprained, though. Was it twisted behind you?"

"Yes." She swallowed again. "He—he pulled it behind me. I thought he'd broken it."

"Don't talk about it now. Eat your soup." He sat beside her on the bed and held the spoon to her lips.

She could only eat a few bites before her throat closed. "I'm sorry. I can't eat any more. It was very good, though."

"There's no need to be quite so polite," he answered with a slight smile, setting the bowl aside. "Not after all we've been through together." Then the teasing light left his light blue eyes and his voice became grim. "Are you feeling sick again?"

"I'm—I—" She leaned her head back, her eyes closing as her voice deserted her.

Joe pulled one of the pillows away and eased her down. "You'll be okay, Lauren. You just need more rest," he told her, smoothing her long, tangled hair away from her face. "Go to sleep."

Sound advice. Lauren sighed and did as he suggested.

The muffled cries of another nightmare summoned Joe to Lauren's bed again during the night. He found her tossing restlessly against the pillow, holding her left arm as though it were hurting her, whimpering softly as the terrifying memories haunted her dreams.

He should have expected another nightmare, he thought in self-censure, leaning over her. After the experience she'd been through, she was likely to be bothered by them for some time to come. "Lauren? Honey, it's okay. It's just another dream. Lauren, can you hear me?"

She stilled, her eyes opening slowly, blearily. "Joe?"

"Yeah, it's me. You okay?"

"Yes," she whispered, then turned her face away from him as though in distress.

He brought it back with a gentle hand, straining to see her in the shadowy light coming through the open doorway from the other room. "Hey, what's this? What's wrong?"

"I feel so stupid. It's not like me to cause so much trouble."

"Don't, Lauren. You're not being stupid. In fact, you're one hell of a gutsy lady."

"No, I'm not." Her voice trembled, one lone tear gleaming against her pale cheek. "They tried to kidnap me, and I was so scared. I'm still scared."

"Not tonight, honey. Don't think about it tonight." Somewhat awkwardly, he wiped her tear with his hand. "Go to sleep now. I'll be right here."

"You need to rest," she protested, though visibly reluctant for him to leave.

"Don't worry about me. I'm not leaving you," he answered firmly.

Lauren turned her bruised cheek into his palm. "I'm glad. Thank you, Joe."

Stunned by his immediate, forceful reaction to the trusting little gesture, Joe could only stare down at her, unable to reply.

Stirring on the pillow, Lauren made herself open her eyes. The light in the room was gray, but she knew it must be morning. The sky must still be cloudy, she decided sleepily, though it sounded as though the rain had finally stopped. Swallowing with difficulty, she turned her head in search of Joe. She found him closer than she'd expected. Rather than sitting in the chair, he was stretched out on the bed beside her, sound asleep. Even in sleep, he lay tensed and poised as if in anticipation of more trouble. She noted that he slept on the very edge of the mattress, probably so as not to disturb her.

Who was this man beside her? She took the opportunity to study him more closely. He seemed...different from the other men she knew, though she couldn't have defined exactly what the difference was. It wasn't his appearance, though he was as handsome close up as she remembered from earlier. She thought him to be in his early thirties. He looked even younger in sleep, with his long, unexpectedly dark lashes lying against his tanned cheeks. His mouth was blatantly sensuous, with a full lower lip and a narrow, expressive upper one. She remembered how his smile had slashed wickedly across his face, causing her heart to flutter ridiculously in response.

Carrying her survey a bit lower, she noted that his bare chest was sleek and tanned, with only a sparse cluster of brown hair in the very center, and his denim-covered legs long and taut. Even in her battered condition, she was not immune to his virility, his magnetism.

Joe. Joe who? Who was he? Why had he been out in the storm at that hour of the night? Why hadn't he asked questions about what had happened to her? Was he being considerate because she'd been so dazed and ill? He'd called her by name—several times—but she didn't remember telling him her name. Had she babbled it during her feverish nightmares?

Her last very clear memory was a desperate, frantic race through storm-whipped woods, her pursuers closing in behind her, her foot slipping in the mud, her arms flailing as she felt herself falling, falling...

She made herself stop thinking about it for now, turning her thoughts deliberately toward more immediate concerns. Trying not to disturb Joe, she eased into a more comfortable position, noting in resignation that both the sheets and her borrowed shirt were different from the last ones she remembered. She tried to tell herself that it didn't matter that a strange man had been entirely responsible for her unconscious body. After all, he *had* saved her life.

She really needed to go to the bathroom. She wondered if she would be able to stand up without passing out. She hated the idea of waking Joe and asking for his assistance in such a personal matter, regardless of the intimacies he'd already been forced to take with her. She wasn't used to being dependent on anyone, much less a total stranger. She didn't like it.

Gathering her strength, she pushed at the blanket covering her and started to ease herself into an upright position.

"I thought I told you not to try to get up again without help," Joe growled.

Startled, her gaze flew to his face. He was lying still, watching her out of those incredibly crystal blue eyes, a frown creasing his brow.

"What do you think you're doing?" he asked. Demanded, really, she thought, beginning to realize that he was a man who didn't often make requests. Giving orders seemed to be more his usual habit.

Her cheeks warm, Lauren answered peevishly. "I think I'm going to the bathroom."

"Not without help, you're not." He stretched, drawing her eyes to the ripple of muscles in his chest, then swung his legs over the side of the bed. "Are you sure you should be doing this?"

She grimaced ruefully, the movement pulling at her bruised face. "Believe me, this is something I need to do."

He swallowed a chuckle, not quite successfully. Lauren forgot her embarrassment and grinned, then wished she hadn't. "God, my face hurts," she muttered.

Joe was at her side, reaching down to help her up. "I'm sure it does. Still, you seem much better than you were yesterday."

"Yes, much," she agreed, somewhat doubtfully. The room spun around her when she came to her feet. She was forced to clutch Joe's bare shoulder with her right hand, her left dangling heavily at her side.

"Hang on, honey," Joe murmured encouragingly, holding her securely. "Breathe deeply."

She obeyed automatically, pulling long, steadying breaths into her lungs. Her ears roared, she was covered in a clammy, acrid sweat, and she saw nothing but gray, but Joe's voice gave her strength. Her vision slowly beginning to clear, she blinked him into focus, noting the concern on his face. She'd caused him too much concern in the past thirty-odd hours. She managed a shaky smile. "I'm all right, Joe."

"Okay. Let's take this slow. Unless you've changed your mind. I can always get the bedpan...."

"No. I can do it," she answered, determined to begin caring for herself—with a little assistance, she added mentally, leaning against his strong shoulder.

The short trip was not possible for her to make alone. Joe ended up carrying her. It was difficult for her to convince him to leave her alone for a couple of minutes, and it took everything she had to get through those minutes without fainting, but she managed.

And then nearly did faint when she staggered to her feet and caught a glimpse of herself in the mirror over the sink.

"Dear God," she whispered, leaning heavily against the vanity.

She hardly recognized the woman who stared back at her in stark horror. Her hair was tangled and filthy, matted with dirt and blood. Her eyes were dull slits in the bruised, swollen skin around them. Her mouth was split and discolored. The little skin not covered with purple bruises was pasty white. There were crusted-over gashes on her forehead and down her right cheek, just in front of her ear. She could only be grateful she couldn't see the rest of her body.

She was still staring into the mirror when Joe opened the door. "Lauren, did you hear me? I've called your name twi—" He stopped, taking in the situation at a glance. His arms went gently around her in support. "Damn," he muttered. "I forgot about the mirror."

"I need a bath and I want to wash my hair," Lauren said forcefully, dragging her gaze away from her reflection.

"Absolutely not." His tone brooked no argument. "This is no time for vanity."

"It's not vain to want to be clean. I'm filthy!" she snapped, trying to jerk away from him, only to be overcome by the sudden movement.

He steadied her when she swayed. "See what I mean?"

"But I—"

"No. Back to bed. You can clean up later, when you're stronger. You need to eat something first."

The thought of food was no more appetizing this time than it had been before, but she knew she must eat to regain her strength—as well as her independence. She nodded grimly.

As she settled gingerly back into the bed, she eyed Joe through her lashes. There were so many questions she wanted to ask, so much she wanted to know, but she didn't know where—or how—to begin.

Joe sat beside her on the bed, one knee pulled up so that he was turned to face her, his expression grave. She'd never considered herself a particularly vain woman, but now she wished he could see her as she usually looked, rather than the way she appeared now. It seemed she'd taken for granted before that men usually found her attractive. If only her hair was clean, or her face free of the disfiguring swelling and bruises....

But she was being ridiculous, of course. She was lucky just to be alive.

Lauren sensed it was time for the questions she'd been expecting from Joe. She didn't blame him, of course. It was only natural he'd have questions of his own. Many of them. She drew a deep breath in preparation of rehashing the ugly memories.

Joe seemed to read her thoughts. He took her right hand in his, his fingers closing around hers in warm support. "Ready to talk about it?"

"No," she answered candidly, "but I know I have to."

He nodded. "Tell me what happened."

Keeping her eyes trained on his face—it seemed easier that way—she complied. "I was in my cabin, reading. It was almost midnight and the storm was getting stronger and the lights had begun to flicker, so I thought I'd turn in for the night."

"You weren't afraid of the storm?"

She shook her head with a slight smile. "No. I like thunderstorms—or at least, I did," she added, her smile fading as she wondered if she'd ever again hear rain and thunder without remembering the terror of that night.

His fingers tightened around hers. "Go on."

She cleared her throat. "I put my book down and started for the bedroom, and then the cabin door burst open behind me. I thought it was the storm, that it had blown open, even though I was sure I'd locked it, so I turned to close it and they... they were there.''

''They?'' Joe prodded.

She nodded. ''Two men. One big, powerful. The other small and wiry.''

''Do you remember what they looked like?''

''Clearly. They didn't even try to hide their faces.''

''Damn.'' He didn't seem pleased by that news. Lauren didn't even want to think about why it seemed to bother him so badly.

She continued. ''The big one looked at the other and said something like, 'That's her. Get her.' They... they were going to take me. I fought them and they hit me and... and hurt me...'' she choked.

''Did they rape you, Lauren?'' Joe interrupted, his jaw rigid, though his eyes were so very gentle.

''No,'' she whispered, and watched as relief crossed his face.

''I didn't think so,'' he murmured, ''but I wanted to be sure.''

She nodded, deeply relieved, as he seemed to be, that she'd been spared that ordeal, at least. ''I managed to get away by biting the big man's hand—hard. I knew the woods better than they did, so I got a head start away from them, though they were closing in on me. And then I fell... the storm drove them away. You know the rest.''

''You said they wanted to kidnap you. Do you know why?'' he asked, watching her steadily.

''Yes.'' She sighed.

''Why?''

''My father.''

''Your—?''

''My father,'' she began again, ''is a prosecuting attorney—*the* prosecuting attorney,'' she added dryly, ''in

Chicago. He's working on the biggest case of his illustrious career, prosecuting a man named Cal Bullock, who is charged with being the leader of the Chosen Ones, a radical, racist hate group based in Chicago. Dad's been preparing his case for months, even has a former gang member hidden away as a witness. There have been a lot of threats against my father, demands for him to deliberately lose the case or to excuse himself from the proceedings. Demands for him to let slip the location of the protected witness. He has refused, of course."

"Of course." The words were repeated with a wry twist she didn't quite understand. Almost as if Joe knew exactly what Marcus Caldwell was like.

"Since I'm his only family," she went on, "he wanted to put me under twenty-four-hour surveillance, lock me into his house with a bevy of bodyguards until the case was settled. I wouldn't go along with that—my father knows how I'd detest being shadowed by bodyguards—but I let him talk me into coming here, to a friend's cabin in the Ozarks. He said I'd be safe here. Obviously I wasn't as safe here as he'd believed I would be."

Joe's pale blue eyes had gone hard and cold. Lauren sensed his anger was directed at her attackers—and was glad it wasn't at her. For the first time since he'd saved her life, she found herself rather intimidated by the almost palpable strength radiating from him. He could be a dangerous man if he chose to be, she realized suddenly, and swallowed hard. "They wanted you as a means of getting to your father," Joe said, drawing her attention back to the conversation.

"Yes. Security around my father is so tight that it would be very difficult to get to him. They obviously thought I'd be an easier target, that they could trade me for the witness. They must have thought my father would be so desperate to get me back that he'd give in to their demands. At the very least, they hoped he'd be distressed enough to drop out of the case. Obviously they don't know my father all that well," she added, her mouth twisting. "Taking me would only make him that much more determined to win his case. He'd be furious, not grief stricken."

Joe lifted an eyebrow at her tone. "You don't think your father would grieve for you? Worry about you?"

She shrugged, avoiding his too-intent gaze. "Of course, he would, in his way. His way is just...different from most people's. And he'd never go along with extortion—not even for me. He'd do everything in his power to get me back, but he wouldn't give in to them."

"You're not very close to him, are you?"

"I love my father," she said after a pause. "But I don't think Marcus Caldwell has ever been really close to anyone or anything, except his work."

"Still, he *was* worried about you. He wanted to keep you safe."

"As I said, he worries in his own way. As bullheaded and unreasonable as he can be, I was almost surprised that he didn't insist that I stay under guard at his house, despite my refusal. It wouldn't have surprised me if he'd had me kidnapped, himself, or something. He doesn't like being turned down. I guess he went along because I finally agreed to come here. I'd rather have stayed home, but anything's better than having someone watching my every move with the excuse of 'protecting' me."

Joe cleared his throat, then changed the subject rather abruptly. "Do you have a job back in Chicago? How were you able to take off at your father's request?"

"I'm self-employed. And I had some free time coming. I usually take the first couple of weeks of May for vacation time."

"What do you do?"

"I'm a CPA. I have a small practice, doing books and tax returns for individuals and a few small businesses. My father thinks I should push to expand and build a large accounting firm, but I like the freedom of staying small and keeping everything on an easily manageable scale. Tax time is always hectic, but during the rest of the year I'm able to enjoy some leisure time." She knew she was telling him more than he probably wanted to know, but it was so much easier to talk about her work than about the terrifying kidnapping attempt that had led to her being here with Joe.

"How long have you been in practice?"

"I opened my office three years ago, after having a midlife crisis and leaving the big corporate world."

He chuckled. "Hardly mid-life. How old are you? Twenty-four? Twenty-five?"

"Twenty-seven. I decided to avoid the rush and have my crisis early."

"You look younger."

"Usually," she admitted. "Though I don't know how you can possibly tell anything about the way I look now."

"I think you look like a beautiful woman who's been through a hell of a lot during the past couple of days," Joe answered, then seemed almost as surprised as Lauren at his words. He cleared his throat. "So, what do you want to do now? Within the next few hours, I mean."

"I don't know," she admitted. "I suppose we should call my father. And the police," she added reluctantly. "Unless you've already called them?" she asked with a sudden frown.

"No."

Her frown deepened. Wouldn't it have been natural for Joe to contact the police after finding a woman beaten and left for dead in a secluded woods? Why hadn't he? "You haven't?"

"No," he repeated, looking just a bit uncomfortable. "I didn't call the police."

"Why not?"

"Because," he admitted, "I was under orders not to let anyone know you were still alive."

Lauren went cold. "Orders?" she asked carefully, drawing back against the pillows. "*Whose* orders?"

"It's not what you think," he assured her hastily, seeing her withdrawal, probably sensing her sudden fear. "You're perfectly safe with me, Lauren."

"*Whose* orders, Joe?" she repeated.

He sighed. "Your father's. I've been your... er, bodyguard since you arrived earlier this week."

Chapter Three

Any disorientation that had lingered after the attack evaporated with Joe's words, leaving Lauren clearheaded and furious. Furious with her father, for hiring a bodyguard despite her refusal, with Joe, for not telling her sooner who he was—and with herself, for having been so dazed and lost after the attack that she'd become dependent upon a man she hadn't known, hadn't even suspected as being more or less than the Good Samaritan he'd seemed.

"You've been my bodyguard?"

He nodded, eyeing her expression warily. "Yeah."

"Ever since I arrived?"

"I got here the day before you did."

The thought of having anyone watching her every move for the past week made her fingers curl into the bed-clothes. "I see."

"Lauren—"

"Obviously you slipped up at your job, since I'm lying here in this condition. What did Dad do, hire a bargain-rate bodyguard? It's not like him to cut corners and pay for anything less than the best."

A muscle twitched in Joe's strong jaw, the only indication that her anger-spurred words had struck home. "I'm aware that I screwed up," he said quietly, his eyes suddenly shuttered. "I'm sorry. Believe me, I wouldn't have had you hurt for anything."

She almost softened at the genuine regret in his deep voice. But, damn, her father made her mad! When she wanted his attention, he ignored her; when she wanted him to leave her alone, he hired someone to follow her around.

Of course, she thought with a hard swallow, if Joe hadn't been following her around, she would probably have died in that stream. She sighed.

"I'm sorry," she said without quite meeting his eyes. "I shouldn't have lashed out at you that way. Obviously this wasn't your fault. It's my father I'm angry with, not you."

"Then you don't really think I'm a bargain-rate bodyguard?"

The hint of amusement in his deep voice brought her eyes swiftly back to his face. If he had the nerve to make fun of her, despite everything, darned if she wouldn't hit him—even though it would probably hurt her more than him at the moment.

He held up a hand. "Never mind. I'm not sure I want you to answer that one. And why are you so annoyed with your father? Surely you know he only acted out of concern for your welfare."

It might make a difference if she truly believed her father had acted out of love or concern for her, rather than for his own convenience. Since she had no intention of discussing her strained relationship with her father with a total stranger—a man who'd been *paid* to take care of her, she reminded herself ruthlessly, aware of a deep, unexplainable disappointment that accompanied the thought— she changed the subject. "You might as well tell me everything," she said brusquely. "What were you told when you were hired? What has been done since I was attacked? Has my father been notified?"

Joe hesitated, as though there were other things he wanted to say first, but finally sighed impatiently and answered her questions. "When I was hired, I was told that your father is working on a dangerously controversial case and that there had been threats against him and his only family—you. He explained your aversion to bodyguards and stressed that I was to watch you without letting you know I was here. He also insisted that I check in by radio every evening at midnight, which is what I was doing when you were attacked."

Hearing the frustrated displeasure in Joe's voice, she risked a glance at him, finding his eyes stormy, his mouth set in a grim line. "You didn't like that."

"No," he admitted. He gestured toward her bruises, her carefully propped sprained arm. "You see why. Unlike your father, I knew what could happen in only twenty minutes. I tried to get him to assign another bodyguard, so we could take shifts watching you. He wouldn't listen to me. He was so confident that you wouldn't be bothered here."

"My father doesn't listen to anyone," she muttered, reluctantly aware of a moment of communion with Joe. She knew him well enough by now to realize that he would hate following orders he didn't agree with. He seemed too accustomed to giving them himself. It occurred to her that he had some things in common with her father, and she felt chilled all over again.

She reminded herself again that he was only with her because her father was paying him to be. That thought had the remarkable effect of steeling her against the attraction she still felt for him. "How long were you supposed to spy on me?"

His eyes hardened at her tone. "Until the end of the case. Your father seems convinced that once Bullock is behind bars, the others will splinter and lose whatever threat they pose. I suggested taking extra precautions for several months after the case ends, just in case of one final act of retribution. He said he'll think about that later."

Lauren nodded. "I got the impression the attack on me was a last act of desperation. They stupidly seem to think that without my father, Bullock has a chance of getting off. And they want the witness—the one they consider a traitor. They want him badly. It seemed as though they were driven more by meanness and fury than by any intelligent, long-range planning."

"Hate mongers aren't exactly known for their intelligence and independent thinking. Usually the leaders round up a following of hairy-knuckled, thick-skulled, easily led morons who are willing to go along with anyone who seduces them with promises of riches and power. Once the leaders are put away, the others will probably scatter."

Lauren bit her lower lip, refusing to smile at his imagery. She resented finding herself in consensus with Joe again, didn't want to forget that he was still her father's employee—and not, as she'd begun to believe, her friend. "Has my father been notified about what happened to me?" she asked again.

"As soon as I found you. He was furious that you were hurt, of course. And that I let it happen."

That startled her, though she realized it probably shouldn't have. "But you were following his orders by leaving me unprotected at midnight."

"Yeah, well, that didn't seem to occur to him—even when I pointed it out."

"My father never accepts responsibility for mistakes. According to him, he's incapable of making them."

"You really do have it in for the guy, don't you?" Joe observed shrewdly.

She squirmed against the pillow. "I've had twenty-seven years to get to know him. As I said, I love him, but that doesn't blind me to his faults."

"If he hadn't hired me, you'd probably be dead by now. You know that, don't you?"

"Yes," she admitted reluctantly. "And I suppose I should be grateful. But I still resent it."

"And you resent me."

She tightened her fingers on the sheets, ignoring the remark. "So what are we supposed to do now?"

"You've been officially listed as missing," Joe replied, going along, for now, with her change of direction. "We thought you'd be safer if no one knows where you are or whether you survived the attack. Your father is doing a convincing job of looking frantic about your welfare even as he proceeds with his preparations for the trial that starts next week. He wants them to think his guard is down when the case begins."

"My father, like most trial attorneys, is a very talented actor."

"For what my opinion is worth, Lauren, he did seem upset about what happened to you. He called several times during that first night to check on you."

She sighed and pushed fretfully at her tangled hair with her right hand. "As I said, he does care—in his own way.

It's just that his way was never as much as I needed from him.'' She stopped abruptly. She hadn't meant to tell Joe so much. He was all too good at drawing her out, despite her resentment of everything he represented.

"I'm sorry, Lauren."

She shrugged, then wished she hadn't when her aching shoulders protested. She bit back a murmur of discomfort. "When will I be leaving here? Is Dad sending someone for me?"

"No. You're staying here until you're up to traveling. And then you and I are finding someplace else to hole up until the trial is over. Somewhere safe, where I can keep an eye on you."

Her eyes widened. "I'm supposed to stay secluded with you, for however many weeks the trial continues?"

"We've all agreed that's the best plan."

"We, who?" she demanded irritably. "You? My father?"

"Yes," he confirmed quietly, meeting her angry eyes without blinking.

"No one thought it necessary to consult *me,* I take it?"

"Be reasonable, Lauren. You were hardly in a condition to make important decisions when I found you."

"That's true," she agreed coolly, "but I'm in much better shape now. Quite capable of thinking for myself."

"And?"

"And I haven't decided whether I'll go along with your plan or not. There are other places I could go."

"Like where?" he challenged.

"I have a very good friend who lives with her husband in St. Louis. They'd be delighted to take me in for a few weeks—they're always asking me to visit."

"Are you willing to risk your good friend's life? Or her husband's?" Joe asked evenly.

Lauren felt herself going pale. "No, of course not."

"That's what you'd be doing. If those two thugs were able to track you to a secluded cabin in the Ozarks, they'd have no trouble tracing you to your friend's house. Next time they might manage to keep you when they grab you—and they wouldn't want to leave witnesses."

Her fingers clutched the sheet so tightly her knuckles ached. "You're trying to frighten me," she accused him, though she wouldn't admit that he was doing an excellent job of it.

"I'm trying to make you see reason. You're safer here—for now. This cabin is even more isolated than the one you were staying in, though it's only a five-minute walk away through the densest part of the woods. It's been rigged for security and I'll be on guard every minute."

He continued to look at her steadily. "I know you have reason to doubt my capability of taking care of you, but I promise you I won't screw up a second time, Lauren. No one's going to hurt you again—not while I'm around to prevent it."

The truth was, Lauren didn't doubt Joe's capability of taking care of her. No one had ever made her feel safer than he had during the long hours since he'd found her. She was tempted to tell him so, found herself wanting to reassure him that she didn't blame him for the attack, but, logically or not, she still found herself resenting that he was in her father's pay. She couldn't help thinking that all his kindness to her, all his tender care, had been motivated more by consideration for his paycheck than for any genuine concern for her.

She'd gotten involved before with someone who worked for her father. A hungry young attorney who'd thought a romance with the boss's daughter was a slick way to facilitate his climb up the professional ladder. Lauren had fig-

ured out his true motivations before it was too late and
saved herself from being totally crushed. But the experience had left her emotionally bruised and wary of getting
too quickly involved again. She told herself that she'd be
especially careful with Joe. She couldn't trust any feelings
that developed under these unsettling, inauspicious circumstances.

"That's it, then. I really have no choice but to stay
here." She spoke in a whisper as she realized just how little control she had over her own life for now. She hated
being out of control.

"Will it really be so bad?" Joe asked carefully. "You
can take the time to rest and recuperate from your injuries. I'll try not to annoy you any more than necessary, and
I'll do everything I can to make you as comfortable as
possible while you recover. What do you say?"

He seemed to be going to quite an effort to gain her
compliance, even though she supposed it wasn't really
necessary. They both knew she had no other options but
to go along with her father's plan—for now. She was
rather surprised that Joe seemed so determined to put her
at ease; she would have said he was more the type to tell her
that she had no choice but to make the best of it. Rather
than allow herself to be softened by the observation, she
told herself he must have decided his job would be easier
with her cooperation.

Okay, she'd cooperate. To an extent, she told herself
firmly. She wouldn't cause any trouble, wouldn't resist
Joe's protection for the duration of the trial. But at no time
during the length of their enforced cohabitation would she
allow herself to forget that he was her father's employee.
That his considerate care of her had been bought and paid
for, just like the care she'd received from the string of

nannies and housekeepers her father had employed after her mother had died when Lauren was only four.

"All right, Joe," she said coolly. "I'll go along with the plan, for now. And I'll tell my father that you handled your job quite capably. You've taken excellent care of me. I'm sure you'll be suitably rewarded."

He frowned, looking genuinely angry with her for the first time. She refused to give in to an impulse to shrink back from that almost palpable anger. As she'd noted before, Joe seemed to be a dangerous man to cross. She could only hope that being the daughter of his client was sufficient protection from his temper. "Fine," he said shortly. "I'll hold you to that."

He pushed himself off the bed, standing straight and tall beside her, his lean body almost vibrating with suppressed irritation. "You need to eat," he said, shoving his hands into the pockets of his worn jeans. "I'll go heat something up and bring it in here."

"Don't bother. I'm not hungry. I'd like to rest for a while."

"Lauren, you should eat something. You have to get your strength back."

"I'm really very tired. I'll eat later." She settled onto the pillows and deliberately turned her back to him. "Thank you, Joe. That will be all for now."

Her breath caught in her throat when a firm yet still gentle hand fell on her shoulder to turn her onto her back. Joe leaned over the bed, his face very close to hers, his eyes glinting like hard, cold, blue diamonds. "Let's get one thing straight before this goes any further," he growled. "I'll take care of you, I'll protect you from anyone who tries to hurt you. But I am *not* your servant. Is that clear, Ms. Caldwell?"

She wouldn't let him see that he intimidated the hell out of her. She lifted her bruised chin and met his furious gaze with her own. "No, you aren't, are you? You're my father's servant. Sorry. I won't forget that again."

"I may be in your father's employ—for the moment—but I'm nobody's servant. Just make sure you don't forget *that*," he retorted before straightening and backing away. "Get some rest," he added in a tone that was nothing less than a direct order. "I'll have a meal ready for you when you wake up."

She didn't quite trust herself to answer. Instead she closed her eyes and blocked him out, not opening them again until she heard the bedroom door close crisply behind him.

Though she hadn't really expected to sleep, her lingering weakness made her drift off. She woke with a start, frowning in response to her various nagging aches before opening her eyes. When she did, she found herself looking at Joe, who sat on the edge of the bed, smiling blandly at her. Apparently he'd gotten over his bad temper and had decided to go back to plan A: keep the client cooperative.

"How long have I been asleep?" she asked without returning the smile.

"Couple hours." He'd showered and shaved since she'd seen him last and had changed into fresh jeans and a white knit shirt that contrasted sharply with his tan. Lauren squirmed on the pillow, intensely aware of her own filthy state. Joe touched her tangled hair. "You could use a bath. Think you're up to it?"

If she hadn't reminded herself immediately who he was and what he represented, she might well have thrown her arms around him. "Yes, I'd love a bath."

His smile deepened a bit at her barely restrained eagerness. "I think it'll make you feel better to be clean. But you have to promise to eat something afterward."

"Blackmail," she said with a sigh. "One of my father's favorite tricks."

Joe's smile faded.

She shrugged, knowing her barb had struck home. "You've got a deal. I'd do almost anything for a bath."

"I've dug out a bathrobe for you to wear. It's mine, so it'll be too big for you, but you can turn back the sleeves and tighten the knot at the waist."

"Can't you bring some of my clothes from my cabin?"

He shook his head. "Can't risk it. Just in case someone's watching the cabin."

She bit her lip at the reminder that she could still be in danger. As a child, she'd often resented her father's work for keeping him away from her for hours, sometimes days at a time. Now she found herself resenting it all over again, for having the potential to ruin—maybe even end—her life. It wasn't that she wanted him to take himself off this case, and certainly not to deliberately lose in court when so much was at stake, but she hated having been put in the middle of it in this manner.

Joe helped her out of the bed, waited a moment until she was certain she was steady on her feet, then ushered her toward the bathroom. "I'll help you with your bath. I've already drawn the water. You—"

Lauren had stopped in midstep. "You'll help me with my bath?" she repeated slowly.

"I'm the only one here. You'd drown if you had to do it alone." Seeing the mutiny she knew must be written on her face, he sighed. "Lauren, I know this isn't easy for you, but you have to realize it's much too late for modesty."

She flushed at the reminder that he'd already seen every inch of her—touched most of what he'd seen. "That doesn't make any difference," she said stubbornly.

"Look, I'll give you as much privacy as I can, but I won't risk having you hurt yourself any further."

She remained silent.

"It's your choice," Joe prodded impatiently. "You can take a bath—with my help—or you can get back in bed dirty."

Again, he sounded so much like her father that she glared at him. "I could really dislike you," she informed him.

Surprisingly enough, he chuckled and touched her cheek with gentle fingers. "Yeah, I know. You work on that while I concentrate on taking care of you, okay? Now, come on. Your water's going to get cold."

The thought of a warm bath proved too much to resist, even when compared to her natural embarrassment at Joe's participation. Refusing to look at him, she took another step toward the open bathroom door.

True to his word, Joe allowed her as much dignity as possible under the circumstances. The bath was blissfully warm and filled with bubbles that smelled of lemons—dish washing detergent, Joe admitted when she gave him a quick look of question. "Hope it's not too harsh," he added. "It said it was gentle to the hands."

"It'll be fine," she assured him a bit gruffly, touched despite herself at the gesture.

He kept his eyes averted as she eased herself out of his oversize T-shirt and while he steadied her as she lowered herself into the water, allowing the bubbles to shield her. Shivering at the accidental brush of his arm against her bare skin, she sank to her chin in the warm water, knowing her cheeks were flaming. Joe moved to the doorway, his back to her, his shoulder propped against the door-frame. "Let me know if you need anything," he said over his shoulder.

"Hmm." She closed her eyes and allowed the water's lemony warmth to soak into her aching muscles.

She could have happily stayed in the tub for hours, but Joe wouldn't allow it. "You're going to drain what little strength you have," he said with another glance over his shoulder a few minutes later. "You've got to get out now."

She sighed. "I know. But...my hair." There was no way she could effectively wash the matted mass with only one hand. Her left arm still hurt much too badly to lift above her waist.

Joe pulled for a moment at his lower lip, then shrugged. "I'll wash it." He reached unceremoniously for the lever that would drain the water from the tub.

Lauren swallowed a gasp of dismay. "No, wait!"

Joe dropped a thick terry towel onto her shoulders just as the bubbles started to dissipate with alarming speed. "Wrap that around you, if you want," he instructed brusquely. "It's okay if it gets wet. I can wring it out and hang it up to dry later."

Chin lowered in embarrassment, she gratefully wrapped the towel around her breasts, noting in relief that it covered everything necessary.

She tipped her head back as he began to wash her hair using a large plastic mug he filled over and over from the running faucet. "Tell me if I'm too rough," he warned her with a slightly crooked grin. "I haven't had a lot of experience at this."

She all but purred under the gentle massage of his fingers as he worked in the shampoo. Maybe Joe wasn't such a jerk, after all, she thought cautiously, even if he *did* work for her father.

* * *

He was a jerk. His hands deep in the mass of her sham-poo-lathered hair, Joe cursed himself steadily, silently, as he scrubbed at the matted mud and blood. The woman was lying here in pain, bruised and swollen and frightened, to-tally dependent on a stranger's care—and he was aching from an arousal so violent that it threatened to break the zipper of his too-tight jeans. He could only hope Lauren wouldn't notice. She really would hate him if she did.

It had been difficult enough to keep his attention off her perfect body while she'd been sick and unconscious. Now that she was awake and regaining her strength and her spirit, he found it impossible. The towel didn't conceal nearly as much as she probably hoped it did. Joe kept his eyes focused sternly on his hands.

He'd been taken aback by the temper she'd displayed when she'd found out who he was, by the snotty tone she'd used to get back at her father through him. She'd almost provoked him into losing his own temper for the first time in longer than he could remember. He usually had himself under better control than that. But once he'd cooled off, he'd found himself reluctantly amused by her flash of spirit.

The stubborn type, apparently. She'd have to be to stand up to her overpowering father. Truth was, Joe had never had much use for compliant, easily managed women. Though he'd been burned on occasion, he still preferred fire over ice.

He squeezed as much water as possible out of the long hair that fell to the middle of her back, then tossed the plastic mug aside. "Let's get you out of there."

He noticed that she was shivering as she climbed out, the fingers of her right hand knotted tightly in the wet towel she held around her. "You're cold," he said with a frown.

"A little."

Snatching up a dry, oversize bath towel, he pulled the wet one away, ignoring her sputtered protests as he briskly dried her before wrapping her in the terry robe. Lauren leaned into his shoulder, trembling with the effort of remaining upright. Joe caught her in his arms and carried her into the living room, where he settled her gently onto one corner of the couch. "I want to dry your hair," he explained, plugging a blow-dryer into a nearby outlet. "I'm afraid you'll catch cold."

Her eyelids looked heavy as she nodded. Joe stood beside the couch and directed a warm flow of air toward her hair, his fingers combing through the tangles in a soothing, rhythmic motion that soon had her nodding, half asleep. "That feels so much better," she murmured. "Thank you."

"You're welcome. Rest, but don't go to sleep. Remember, you promised you'd eat."

She murmured her disinterest in the subject, and settled more comfortably into the corner of the couch, her injured arm draped across her lap. Looking down at her, Joe decided in resignation that she was already asleep. Though still bruised and swollen, she looked remarkably improved after her bath. Her long hair was drying, beginning to gleam softly in the lamplight. She had the most beautiful hair he'd ever seen, dark blond mingled with a hint of red—the color of rich, sweet honey—so soft it was all he could do not to bury his face in the strands that slipped so seductively through his fingers.

His body ached again with a surge of hunger he had no immediate hope of satisfying. He tried to block out thoughts of her nude body, glowing from the warmth of the bathwater, soft and fragrant and pliant beneath his hands as he'd dried her. Grinding a curse from between clenched teeth, he snapped off the dryer and forced himself to turn away, heading grimly toward the bathroom to clean up in there and change the bedclothes before moving into the kitchen to warm her meal.

He really deserved a medal after this case, he decided with a wry attempt at humor. Giving Lauren a bath had definitely ranked above the call of duty. Some might even have called it torture. Damned sweet torture.

Lauren stood at the bedroom window, staring out into the darkness, her left arm cradled carefully in front of her. The cabin was quiet behind her, the bedroom deeply shadowed, the only illumination coming from a dim nightlight low on one wall. The only sounds were those of the mountain wildlife—crickets, frogs, owls, a few animal cries she couldn't identify. Yet nothing out there frightened her as much as her own thoughts.

"Can't sleep?"

She'd gotten so accustomed to Joe's silent approaches that they no longer startled her. She'd thought him asleep, hadn't seen him in hours, since he'd all but forced a bowl of soup down her and then carried her back to bed despite her protests that she'd been perfectly capable of walking. Without turning around, she answered him. "No."

He was close behind her when he spoke again. "Are you in pain?"

"Not really. There's still some discomfort, of course, but nothing I can't handle."

"If it gets any worse, let me know."

"Thank you, but I'm fine. I'm feeling much better, really."

He seemed to mull that over for a moment, then asked, "Did you have another bad dream?"

She shook her head, her clean hair swaying against her back with the movement. "No. I guess I'm just not sleepy. Heaven knows, I've gotten enough sleep in the past two days." Forty-eight hours, she thought, focusing fiercely on an oddly shaped tree silhouetted against a bright half moon. It had only been forty-eight hours since... She made a deliberate effort to blank her mind. A futile effort.

Joe's hands settled gently on her shoulders, warm through the borrowed T-shirt she was wearing. "Try not to think about it, Lauren. You're safe now."

"How can I stop thinking about it?" she whispered. "Someone wants to hurt me. People I don't know, that I've never harmed. I don't understand..."

He drew her back against his warm, bare chest, his arms encircling her, careful of her injuries. She didn't resist, though she knew she should. At the moment she needed his strength more than she needed to be wary of him. "I know, Lauren."

He sounded as though he did understand, as if he'd been there himself. Who was he? she found herself wondering, not for the first time. How had he ended up working for her father, presumably with the skills to protect her life, if necessary?

"I know you're frightened," he murmured against her hair. "But if it helps, I'm here. And anyone who wants to get their hands on you is going to have to go through me first."

She turned then, without breaking the contact between them, staring up at his shadowed face. "Who are you, Joe? Where did my father find you?"

He hesitated. "Can't you just think of me as a friend for now?" he asked quietly.

"I wish I could," she whispered, closing her eyes and resting her forehead against his shoulder.

His arms tightened carefully around her. "Why can't you?"

"Nothing like this has ever happened to me before. I've always taken charge of my own life, as much as possible, but now I don't know what to do. I don't know who to turn to."

"Turn to me."

"I don't know you. You're a stranger. And you work for my father."

"Only for now. And only to protect you."

She took a deep breath, let it out shakily. "I'm scared."

"Of the men who tried to hurt you? That's only natural."

"Yes, of them. And..."

"Of me?" He said the words without offense. "That's only natural, too. You don't know me. You have only my word that I'll do everything I can to keep you from being hurt again."

"Who *are* you?" she asked again, finally lifting her head to look at him.

He hesitated for a long time, then dropped the lightest of kisses on her forehead. "Ask me again sometime," he murmured before stepping away from her. "Try to go back to sleep now. We'll talk more tomorrow."

He tucked her in as tenderly as a child, but something in his face when he looked down at her told her he didn't think of her as a child at all. "Good night, Lauren."

"Good night," she whispered.

He left her wishing that he would sleep beside her again, as he had the night before, and angry with herself for even acknowledging these feelings that she shouldn't have, couldn't trust. Her whole world was turned upside down,

she thought wearily. She was too vulnerable, too frightened to know how to interpret her feelings—or his actions. She had to keep remembering that.

But it was the feel of Joe's arms around her, his lips
brushing her forehead that lingered with her as she closed
her eyes and drifted back into sleep.

Chapter Four

Lauren felt so well when she woke the next morning that she couldn't bear the thought of any more time in bed. She sat up carefully, pleased that the resulting dizziness was mild and very short-lived. Joe's thick terry bathrobe was draped over the chair beside the bed. She wasn't enthusiastic about wearing it again, but was hesitant to raid his closet without his permission. Sighing, she slipped into the robe and belted it in front of her as best she could with the limited use of her still sore left arm.

She washed up and then struggled to pull the tangles out of her hair with the comb she found lying on the bathroom sink, thinking longingly of her own clothing and toiletries in the cabin so close to this one. Though she wouldn't argue with him about the subject again, she still thought Joe was being overly cautious in not retrieving some of her things.

Joe's mind wouldn't be easily changed once he'd made his decisions, she mused, trying to avoid her battered-looking reflection in the mirror. She'd save her arguments with him for more important issues—and something told her there would be occasions for them to argue. She had no intention of meekly standing back and allowing Joe to dictate her every action for the next few days, or weeks, or however long it took to convince him and her father that she was safe.

Smoothing the robe with her right hand, she hesitated for a moment in front of the bedroom door, then took a deep breath and turned the knob. A doorway on the other side of the minimally furnished living room opened into a rather primitive kitchen. Bright sunlight streamed through the somewhat grimy window over the sink, and appetizing aromas scented the air. Joe stood in front of an old gas stove, stirring something in an iron skillet. As though sensing her presence behind him, he turned to greet her with a smile. "Good morning."

Her knees went weak—a reaction to his charmingly crooked smile rather than her injuries. She propped her good hand on the doorjamb. "Good morning."

"Are you hungry?"

"Ravenous," she admitted.

"I thought you might be. Have a seat. Breakfast is almost ready."

Lauren couldn't even remember the last time a man had cooked breakfast for her. Smiling at the novelty of it, she slid into one of the four bow-backed oak chairs placed around the round oak pedestal table. Joe handed her a steaming cup of coffee. "You want cream and sugar with that?"

"No, I drink it black." Braced for the worst, she took a sip, then lifted her eyebrows in pleased surprise. "This is really good."

He chuckled. "You were expecting it to be bad?"

"Most men seem to make coffee strong enough to strip paint. This is just right."

"Yeah, well, I'm not like most men," he drawled, setting a well-filled plate in front of her.

"I noticed," she murmured, looking at her breakfast. "Are we supposed to share this plate?"

"No, I'll have one of my own." He sounded amused by her question.

Looking at the mountainous serving of scrambled eggs, the six slices of crisp bacon, the fried potatoes and oversize biscuits overflowing her plastic plate, Lauren shook her head. "You surely don't expect me to eat all this myself."

"You haven't had more than a few bites in a couple of days. You need to rebuild your strength before we move on."

She picked up her fork. "If I keep eating like this, I'll be too fat to move on."

Holding an equally loaded plate, he dropped into the chair opposite her, his lazily thorough inspection making her vividly self-conscious of her disheveled appearance. "You're a long way from being fat," he said after a moment.

She concentrated fiercely on slicing into a fried potato.

"You look like you're feeling better. How's the arm?" Joe asked after they'd eaten in silence for a few minutes.

"*I'm* feeling a lot better, though my *arm* is still pretty sore." She savored another bite of bacon. Always conscious of her weight and health, it had been a long time since she'd allowed herself to eat like this. She'd almost forgotten how pleasurable culinary decadence could be. Now if only she had some chocolate to finish it off...

She realized Joe had said something else while she'd been wallowing in calories. "I'm sorry, what did you say?"

He repeated, "I'm supposed to check in with your father in an hour. I thought you might like to speak with him when I do."

Her appetite diminished measurably. She set down her fork and reached for her coffee. "Yes, of course," she said, hearing the lack of enthusiasm in her reply.

"You don't want to speak to him?"

"Of course I do," she answered, a bit peevishly. "Didn't I just say so?"

To her relief, he let the subject drop, standing to retrieve the coffeepot from the stove. "Want me to heat that up for you?"

"Yes, thank you."

His arm brushed her shoulder as he leaned over her to refill her cup. Though she told herself she was being ridiculous, she could have sworn her skin tingled through the terry-cloth robe where he'd made contact. She shook her head, thinking that she must still be feeling the effects of the concussion. How else could she explain the way she reacted to this man? This stranger?

But he didn't seem like a stranger when he slid back into his chair and gave her a faint smile across the table before picking up his fork and turning his attention to his food again. There was a sense of intimacy between them, as though they'd long been accustomed to breakfasting together. An oddly domestic feeling that made Lauren yearn for something she couldn't have defined had she tried at the moment.

And suddenly she realized that she was sharing breakfast with a man whose last name she didn't even know.

"What *is* your last name, anyway?" she blurted without thinking.

Joe lifted an eyebrow at the abrupt question. "Does it matter?"

"Well, of course it matters," she replied, startled by his response. "After all, we are living together—temporarily, at least."

"Living together," Joe repeated musingly, his crystalline eyes glinting with what might have been teasing humor. "Yes, I suppose we are—in a rather dull sort of way."

She fought a smile of response, forcing a frown of reproval instead. "You know what I mean."

He shrugged. "I know what you mean."

She waited another moment, then asked again, "Are you going to tell me or not?"

He downed half his coffee before asking, "Tell you what?"

Lauren sighed gustily. "Your name."

"Joe." He set down the cup and popped the last bite of bacon into his mouth.

"*Damn,* you're infuriating."

He smiled. "So I've been told."

She mentally counted to ten, trying to decide whether it was worth pursuing. For some reason, she decided it was. "All right, one more time. We've established that your name is Joe. Joe what?"

He abandoned the teasing and gave her a steady look that made her feel as though she'd been just a bit presumptuous to ask in the first place. "I haven't used the same last name more than a few months at a time for the past fifteen years. Just call me Joe, unless you'd like me to make up a last name to pacify you?"

"No," she said, her mind whirling with questions about this mysterious, utterly frustrating man. "That won't be necessary."

"Good. Can I get you anything else to eat?"

"No. Thanks."

"How are you feeling? Want to lie down for a little while before we call your father?"

"No," she said again quickly. "Believe me, I don't want to go back to bed. I think I'd die of boredom if I had to go back to that bed."

Joe's mouth tilted again into that disarmingly roguish smile. "I suppose that would depend on the circumstances."

She chose to ignore him. "I'm equally tired of this robe, comfortable as it is. Are you sure you can't sneak into my cabin and bring me back a change of clothes?"

He appeared to consider it for a moment, raising her hopes, but then he dashed them again by shaking his head. "Too risky. I don't want to leave you alone here, and I certainly don't want to risk leading anyone to you."

"Do you really expect me to sit around naked for however long we're stranded together?" she demanded, the imprudent words spurred by frustration.

He choked on the last sip of his coffee. "Uh, no," he said after a moment. "I'm sure we can come up with something out of my closet to fit you."

Cursing her impulsive tongue, she nodded and mumbled a thank you.

After clearing the kitchen, Joe fulfilled his promise and found some clothing for Lauren—a pair of drawstring-waist gray sweatpants, white tube socks, and a black pocket T-shirt. "Not exactly high fashion," he said with a hint of apology. "But it's all I've got that would come anywhere close to fitting you."

She took the garments gratefully. "These will be fine," she assured him. "Thank you."

He stepped to the door of the bedroom. "I'll leave you to get dressed, then. Can you manage with your arm?"

"I'll manage."

He nodded. "Yell if you need help. I'll be in the living room." He closed the bedroom door behind him before she could respond.

Lauren released a shaky breath—she found herself doing that a lot after being with Joe, she realized—and allowed his robe to fall from her shoulders. She wondered how much longer this would go on. And she wondered, half-seriously, who was more dangerous: the fumbling bullies who'd tried to kidnap her... or Joe.

Joe was at the radio when Lauren stepped out of the bedroom a short time later. Something about his set expression told her that he wasn't at all happy with whomever he'd been talking to. It must be her father, she decided resignedly.

Joe glanced up at her and apparently made an effort to lighten his expression. "Yes," he said into the headset, "she's right here. Hold on." He tugged the headset off and held it out to Lauren. "It's your father. The signal's scrambled, so you don't have to watch what you say."

"All right." She allowed Joe to help her don the headset, then sat in the chair he'd vacated for her. "Dad?"

The booming voice in her ear made her flinch. "Lauren? Honey, I'm really sorry about what happened. Are you all right?"

"I'm okay, Dad. A few aches and bruises, but nothing serious."

"I'm glad to hear that. I thought it best not to leave here when the case was at such a critical point, but I'd have dropped everything and come straight to you if Joe had even hinted that you were hurt seriously. You know that, don't you?''

"Yes, of course," she replied obediently, though she wasn't at all sure she really believed him. "How is the case going?''

"It's going great," he answered, all but crowing his satisfaction. "I've got the opposition so confused they have no idea what's going on. As far as everyone here knows, you've disappeared and I'm half-distraught with worry. They have no clue that I'm still putting together an iron-clad case for the prosecution.''

"That's brilliant, Dad." Did anyone really believe that cold-bloodedly single-minded Marcus Caldwell was "half-distraught" with worry about his only daughter? Lauren tried to ignore her own skepticism. "Is your witness still cooperating?''

"Oh, yeah. The fool's ready to spill his guts—anything to buy himself some leniency from the court. Stupid bastard," he added in a mutter that showed his distaste for the man who would betray his former friends, even though Marcus had no qualms about using that betrayal for his own purposes.

"When will it be over, Dad?''

Caldwell hesitated a moment before answering. "I don't know, Lauren. You know how these things can drag on sometimes. But I promise I'll do everything I can to wrap it up as quickly as possible. Once Bullock's behind bars, you'll be safe. There'll be no reason for any of his lackies to harass you then. In the meantime, I've got a whole team out looking for the two men who attacked you. Joe's passed on your descriptions of them and we think we know who they are. They're still missing, but we'll find them. I swear.''

"And in the meantime?"

"In the meantime, we're going to make sure you're safe. I was just telling Joe that I want you out of that area as soon as you're up to traveling. I've got a beach cabin in Galveston lined up for you to use next. Joe's not so sure about it, but I've checked it out. It's a safe place for you.

"By the way, honey," he added in the same breath, "if you want another bodyguard, you just say the word. I'll have one there in an hour."

"Why would I want another?" she asked with a frown. "Don't you think one is sufficient?"

"I didn't mean in addition to Joe," Marcus clarified. "I meant as a replacement for him. I'd certainly understand if you have qualms about him, since he's already failed to protect you once."

Lauren stiffened in indignance on Joe's behalf. "Since Joe was only following your orders by leaving me unprotected for a short time that night, I have no reason to doubt his competence at his job," she informed her father coolly. "If I must have a bodyguard, I'd prefer to remain with the one I know rather than having to depend on another stranger. As for where we'll go next, I'll defer to whatever Joe thinks best. For now."

"Lauren—"

"I'm sure you need to get back to your work, Dad. Thank you for your concern, but the best thing you can do for me now is to bring this case to a close so I can get back to my life."

"I'm giving it everything I've got, Lauren."

"I'm sure you are, Dad. You've always given everything you had to your job," she answered with a trace of sadness. She pulled off the headset and handed it to Joe. "I'll be in the kitchen," she told him, avoiding his eyes. "I need something to drink."

"We have juice and sodas in the refrigerator," he told her, eyeing her closely as he stood poised by the radio.

She nodded and turned away, leaving Joe to talk to the man who was paying him to take care of her.

Joe gave Lauren ten minutes of privacy after he brought the call to her father to a rather abrupt end. After seeing her expression when she'd walked out of the room, he'd decided she needed some time to herself. He didn't know exactly what Caldwell had said to her, but he sensed that the relationship between father and daughter was strained. And that Lauren was the one who suffered most because of it.

The silence from the kitchen finally bothered him so badly that he couldn't resist going to check on her. He found her sitting at the table again, an untouched glass of juice in front of her, her eyes locked on the window over the sink.

"You okay?" he asked, feeling awkward and intrusive as he shoved his hands into his pockets and watched her.

"Yes, fine." Her voice was cool, distant, utterly composed. Like her expression. "Did you and my father come to an agreement on what we're going to do next?"

"We'll be staying here at least another thirty-six hours. There's no reason to think the men who attacked you are still in the vicinity. Someone's been watching your cabin and no one has approached it since I found you. In a day or two, we'll move on. We haven't decided where yet."

Her fingers clenched around her juice glass until her knuckles whitened. Had Joe not been watching her hand, he would have missed her sole reaction to his words. He sensed that it bothered Lauren greatly to have so little say in her actions for the next few days, or possibly weeks. From what little he'd observed of her so far, he could tell that she wasn't accustomed to being told what to do, or to meekly obeying orders—her father's, or anyone else's, apparently.

But she only nodded and kept her eyes trained on the small, grimy window, as though her thoughts were far away from this isolated Ozarks cabin. Far away from him. He found himself resenting the distance, tempted to do something unexpected to fully reclaim her attention.

He wasn't prepared when she spoke again, asking a question that caught him completely off guard. "What was your father like?" she asked, turning her gaze to his face.

"*My* father?" he repeated, frowning.

"Yes. What was he like? When you were growing up, I mean."

Joe thought of a distant, drunken stranger brooding in a battered chair in a crowded, drafty, run-down rent house. "From what little I remember of him, my father wasn't a very pleasant man," he said.

"I'm sorry."

"No need to be. He's been dead a long time."

Lauren sighed and looked down at her glass. "When I was little, I used to dream of a TV-type daddy who'd always be there for me with hugs and tickles and words of wisdom. You know, the fathers on all those situation comedies depicting annoyingly perfect families."

Joe gave a wry chuckle. "The television generation. I always wanted a real 'Pa,' like Lucas McCain from 'The Rifleman' or Ben Cartwright from 'Bonanza.' I was a Western fan," he added unnecessarily. "Always rushed home from school to catch the afternoon reruns."

"And brothers and sisters," Lauren said, still lost in her own thoughts. "I wanted a whole houseful. I thought it wouldn't matter if Daddy wasn't around much if only I had a big family to take his place. Instead, it was just me and nannies and housekeepers and the occasional playmate I was allowed to bring home for slumber parties.''

"Sounds lonely.''

"Yes, sometimes. Do you have brothers and sisters, Joe?''

He thought grimly of a houseful of children torn apart by the deaths of their alcoholic father and life-defeated young mother. It had been a very long time since he'd allowed himself to remember.

He ran a hand through his hair. "My family was split up when I was just a kid. I've been on my own for a long time.''

"Do you ever wish it were different?'' she asked, watching him gravely.

"Wishing is a waste of time,'' he replied gruffly. "I've learned to deal with life the way it is, not the way I'd like it to be.''

"Maybe that's best,'' she mused.

"I've always thought so.''

Lauren pushed a heavy lock of hair away from her face and took a long swallow of her juice. And then she looked back at the window with an expression of sudden determination. "I want to go outside. I need some fresh air.''

"I don't know, Lauren . . .''

"I want to go out, Joe,'' she said flatly. And then, more pleadingly, "Just for a little while.''

"You don't even have a pair of shoes,'' he pointed out, though he found his resolve weakening in response to the look in her large green eyes.

"You could lend me a pair. Please.''

Ah, hell. Joe blew out a short breath and stood, his chair scraping against the scarred wooden floor. "All right. Come on. But we'll have to stay close to the cabin.''

"Fine, as long as I can be outside for a few minutes."

He didn't like it, but he couldn't tell her no. Not after seeing the expression in her eyes when she'd talked about the father she so obviously loved, despite everything. "Wait here. I'll find you some shoes."

Her smile was a weak attempt. "Thank you."

The tennis shoes Joe found for her were sizes too big, but Lauren laced them tightly and kept them on by sliding her feet rather than lifting them. "They'll do, since we're not going far," she said, eager to be out of the suddenly stuffy confines of the tiny cabin.

Joe nodded. She could tell by his grim expression that he still didn't like the idea of taking her out into the open, but she was grateful that he'd agreed. She couldn't have fully explained it, but she really needed to be outside, if only for a few minutes. She frowned when he reached into the drawer of a table in the living room and pulled out a handgun. The sight of the weapon in his large, tanned hand made her shiver. "I don't like guns," she said.

He shrugged and stuck it in the back waistband of his jeans, apparently accustomed to wearing it there.

Something else for her to think about later.

Restlessly adjusting the makeshift handkerchief sling he'd insisted she use to support her left arm, she asked crossly, "Do you really expect me to like being followed around by an armed man?"

"I didn't ask you to like it," he said without expression. "It's either this, or we stay inside."

She could tell he wasn't bluffing. She sighed and conceded without grace. "All right. Come on, then."

His hand on her arm stopped her when she would have stepped toward the door. "I'll go out first."

An expressive roll of her eyes was all she allowed herself in response.

The cabin had been built almost into the base of a tall hill, so that it was all but hidden by the rising ground behind it and the thick underbrush around it. Towering trees loomed overhead, their thickening leaves casting the cabin and its surroundings into deep shadow in most places. A tumbledown outbuilding stood to one side, and a few leaning power poles, laced together by the wiring they supported, trailed off into the woods toward the main roads to the east. A road that was little more than a dirt path led away from the cabin and disappeared alongside the power poles, which were the only sign that the cabin wasn't entirely isolated from civilization.

A flash of movement out of the corner of her eye made Lauren turn, aware that Joe had already whirled in that direction. A doe, closely followed by a long-legged fawn, bounded out of sight, startled by the sight and smell of humans. Lauren turned eagerly back to Joe. "Weren't they beauti—?"

Her voice trailed away at the sight of the gun in his hand. He gave her a rather sheepish smile and stuck it back in his jeans.

Lauren scowled. "You thought maybe the deer were armed?" she asked sarcastically.

"I'm only doing my job," he replied, returning the frown.

She shook her head and turned away, taking a few steps toward the outbuilding. The air was warm and fragrant, and the songs of dozens of birds floated down from the treetops. Lauren would have found the outing pleasant and relaxing had it not been for Joe. He stood so close to her that she could almost feel the tension radiating from his coiled muscles, his hand twitching occasionally as though he were just itching to reach again for the gun. His eyes were narrowed and constantly moving, scanning the road, the trees, the underbrush.

After less than fifteen minutes, Lauren finally sighed and threw up her hands in resignation. "Let's go back in. I can't enjoy being out here with you acting as though we're going to be ambushed at any moment."

He winced, but turned without protest toward the cabin. She could tell he wasn't going to argue with her, since he'd rather go back inside, anyway.

As she walked into the cabin, Lauren realized that she was tired. It annoyed her very much that she was still so weak from her injuries even after sleeping so much during the past few days, and she wouldn't have admitted her weariness to Joe for anything. She moved as nonchalantly as possible toward her bedroom door, thinking that a short nap would do wonders for her.

Joe stopped her with a hand on her arm. "Lauren?"

"I thought I'd lie down for a few minutes," she said, ready for some time to herself.

"I'm sorry I spoiled your outing."

The low-spoken apology took her by surprise. "As you said, you were only doing your job."

He nodded. "Right. I don't want to take any unnecessary risks with your safety. I'm not screwing up again."

He dropped his hand from her arm and started to turn away. This time it was Lauren who reached out to stop him. "I don't want you to blame yourself because I got hurt, Joe. Whatever my father might have said to you, you did nothing wrong. You saved my life."

He searched her face for a moment, as though to confirm that she meant what she said. And then he gave her a faint, one-sided smile and leaned over to brush his lips across her cheek, so lightly that she hardly felt his touch.

"Thanks for the vote of confidence. Now go lie down. You look tired."

So much for trying to fool him.

She stepped rather dazedly into her bedroom, closed the door behind her, then lifted her fingertips to her cheek. He'd kissed her. And though it had been no more than a fleeting caress, her entire body had tingled in response.

Fool.

She would *not* allow herself to become involved with this man, she reminded herself as she sank to the edge of the bed. There were too many reasons to be cautious. She was particularly vulnerable at the moment, totally dependent on Joe, who'd already saved her life once. He was being paid to take care of her—well paid, most likely. Her father had always believed in paying generously for services rendered. And Joe had given her little reason to believe that he saw her as anything more than a challenging assignment.

He was definitely an attractive man—sexy, charming when he chose to be, intriguingly mysterious—and the enforced intimacy of their circumstances naturally formed a bond, of sorts, between them. But she would only be hurt—hurt badly, perhaps—if she started reading more into it than that.

"You don't even know his last name, Lauren," she reminded herself in a murmur as she settled into the pillow. "A man like Joe doesn't need anyone. Don't forget that."

And she wouldn't need him, she decided, closing her eyes and allowing her tense muscles to relax. Not once this mess was behind her. Not when she returned to her own life, her own world. She depended on him now, but she could keep it in perspective.

Maybe.

* * *

Joe paced the cabin, restless, tense, all too aware of the silence coming from Lauren's bedroom, fighting the temptation to check on her. He knew full well that it was only an excuse to look at her again while she slept.

He was getting too involved. He, of all people, should know better than to get involved with an assignment, especially after what had happened to Ryan, the only person in the world Joe really cared about. Ryan had almost lost his life because he'd allowed himself to be distracted by a woman during a case. He'd spent a week in a coma and nearly a year in recovery because of it. That had been two years ago, and both Joe and Ryan had been extremely careful about their relationships since.

Besides, he mused grimly, there was no reason to believe that Lauren would have looked twice at him had they met under other circumstances. He was a rover with no last name and a shady background. She was the daughter of a wealthy, powerful man and had a successful, stable career of her own. He knew from experience about women like that. They got their kicks with guys like him for a while, but when it came time to make commitments, they looked for upwardly mobile businessmen from their own social circles.

His suddenly overactive libido would just have to be ignored while he concentrated on keeping Lauren Caldwell safe and returning her to her jerk of a father. Then they'd both get back to their lives, this interlude nothing but a hazy memory to both of them.

Maybe.

Chapter Five

Lauren woke with a startled gasp when someone roughly shook her sometime during the night. She blinked against the dim light coming from the nightstand. "What . . . ?"

"It's me." Joe's voice was low, hard-edged.

She stared at him, slowly focusing, noting the grave expression on his face. "What is it?"

"The perimeter alarms have been activated. It may only be a large animal, but I'm not taking any chances. I'm going out to investigate."

She sat up, reaching for his arm. "You're going out alone?"

"Yeah. I'll be okay."

"What about me?"

He put something cold and heavy in her hand. "You know how to use that?"

She looked down at the gun with a shudder of distaste. "No."

He did something to the mechanism—she assumed he was releasing the safety—then stepped back. "Just point it in the general direction and pull the trigger. If nothing else, you'll scare the hell out of anyone in front of you. But do me a favor first, make sure it's not me you're shooting at, okay?"

"Joe—"

He touched her cheek. "I've got to go out. I won't be long. You'll be safe, Lauren."

"Be careful."

"I always am," he assured her, and slipped out of the room with a lethal stealth that left her wondering again just who this man was who felt so at ease in a potential crisis.

It seemed like hours that he was gone. Her heart pounded in her throat the entire time, her hands clenched painfully around the gun, her eyes trained almost without blinking on the bedroom door. She found herself praying—not for herself, but for Joe. Was he all right? What if he . . . ?

A sound from the other room made her swallow hard and tighten her grip on the weapon. Would she be able to use it if she had to? Would she be able to hit anything if she did?

"Don't shoot." Joe's voice preceded him into the room by mere seconds.

Lauren's eyes closed on a brief prayer of gratitude. She opened them quickly and reached out to Joe as he approached the bed, forgetting the gun for a moment.

He swiftly relieved her of it and snapped the safety back on. "Remind me to give you some lessons in how to use this."

"What did you find?"

He shook his head. "Nothing except a few tracks I don't particularly like. We're leaving tomorrow," he added without bothering to consult her about the decision.

It wasn't easy for her to accept his high-handedness without protest, but lingering fear made her swallow her rebuke and nod. "All right."

"Try to get some more sleep. You'll need your strength for traveling."

She doubted that she'd be able to sleep now, but she nodded again, knowing Joe needed rest.

Joe's gaze narrowed on her face. "You okay?"

"Yes. Just a little shaken," she admitted.

He smoothed a strand of her sleep-tousled hair away from her eyes. "That's understandable. Will you be okay in here alone? Want me to stay with you? I can catch a nap in the chair."

She shook her head, bringing her cheek in contact with his hand. "I'll be fine, Joe. You get some rest."

"Okay. But I'm right next door if you need me."

"I know. Thanks."

His smile lightened his dark expression. "No problem."

He hesitated another long moment, his hand against her cheek, his eyes locked with hers. She thought he was going to kiss her again and, despite her better judgment, she had no intention of resisting if he did. She was disappointed when he did nothing more than stroke her cheek with his fingertips and then step back from the bed.

"Good night, Lauren," he said, snapping off the lamp. "I'll wake you when it's time to get ready to leave."

"Good night, Joe."

He started to close the door behind him. She stopped him. "Would you leave it open?"

"Of course. Mine will be open, too."

She settled back down into the pillows, taking some comfort in the thought that he would only be a few feet away, and that there would be no closed doors between them. She couldn't help remembering the night he'd slept beside her and wishing he were here now. She tried to tell herself she wanted him beside her only because she felt safer that way. But she knew even as the thought crossed her mind that she wasn't being entirely truthful.

They left at daybreak in a battered Jeep that had been hidden in the weed-overgrown outbuilding. Lauren wore the sweatpants and T-shirt again, to her dissatisfaction, but Joe promised to buy her something to wear as soon as they arrived in Galveston. He'd decided to accept her father's assurances that the beach cottage there would be a safe place to hide out, and had already been in contact with Caldwell to let him know they were on their way there.

"I hope you're up to traveling that far," he fretted as he made sure she was strapped into her seat.

Touched by the genuine concern in his eyes, she gave him a reassuring smile. "I'm fine, Joe. Really."

And she *was* fine, she decided during the bumpy trip down the mountain. Her head no longer hurt, though the bruises were still prominent against her fair skin. The scrapes were healing and the aches receding. Even her left arm felt much better, though she still wore the sling to support it. Joe had taken very good care of her during the past three days since he'd rescued her.

She reminded herself yet again that he was being well paid to do so. She had to keep telling herself that, or it would be much too easy to believe he was taking care of her because he genuinely cared about her.

The beach cottage Caldwell had provided was a better safe house than Joe had pessimistically expected. Located at the far west end of Galveston Island, it was rigged with what appeared to be an excellent security alarm system, was isolated enough that he could easily spot anyone approaching, yet within sight of other vacation homes. Caldwell had arranged for the cottage to be fully stocked, even providing books, tapes, clothing and toiletries for Lauren, to her pleasure.

Joe didn't like the pallor in Lauren's cheeks or the lines that had formed around her eyes and mouth during the chartered flight from Little Rock. Though she hadn't complained, he knew she'd tired during the trip. He insisted she lie down as soon as they arrived at the cottage. It was a measure of her weariness that she did so without putting up an argument. She even gave him a wan smile as she left the living room, heading for the bedroom he'd assigned her.

Hearing the bedroom door close behind her, Joe tugged thoughtfully at his lower lip. Oddly enough, he preferred her obstinate and resistant rather than wearily compliant. Lauren's stubborn, tenacious nature—the fiery spirit that had made her cling to that stream bank against all odds, and let her hold her own against a father who was more than a little overpowering—was one of the things he admired most about her.

Realizing that he was still standing in the spot where she'd left him, staring wistfully at her bedroom door, he muttered an impatient curse and turned away.

Lauren wasn't quite sure what had changed between her and Joe during the flight to Texas, but for some reason neither of them seemed to be able to relax during their first evening in the beach cottage.

Joe had a meal prepared when she woke from her exhaustion-lengthened nap. Lauren forced a smile as she slid into one of the four chairs at the café-style breakfast table and picked up her fork. "You're going to spoil me if you keep cooking for me like this," she said, looking appreciatively at the broiled chicken breast and steamed vegetables on her plate. "I'll have to take my turn at KP tomorrow."

Joe shrugged. "I don't mind cooking. It beats a steady diet of hamburgers and pizza. Although there've been times when I was glad to get those," he added.

The subject of food exhausted, Lauren tried to think of some other conversational gambit to fill the noticeable silence between them as they ate. She knew so little about Joe, especially considering how intimate they'd been during the past few days. There was so much she wanted to know about him, so many questions she longed to ask, but she wasn't at all sure he'd welcome them. He hadn't even been willing to tell her his last name. All she knew about him was that his father hadn't been a nice man and his family had been split up years ago.

It really wasn't fair, she reflected, swallowing a tender bite of carrot. He knew so much about her—including the shape of the birthmark high on her right thigh!—and she didn't even know where her father had found him for this assignment. That, at least, was one question she could ask without hesitation. After all, it concerned his qualifications for keeping her safe. "Do you work for a security agency in Chicago, Joe?"

He shook his head. "Not in Chicago." And then he lifted his glass and took a deep swallow of iced tea, apparently satisfied that he'd answered her question.

Lauren persisted. "Where *do* you work?"

"Wherever I'm assigned."

He was, without doubt, the most frustrating, infuriating man she'd ever met. And the most fascinating, she added reluctantly, taking a deep breath for patience. "Why do you insist on evading all my questions about you? Don't you think I have a right to know something about the man who is responsible for keeping me alive for the next few weeks?"

He had the grace to look slightly repentant. "There's really not all that much to know," he said after a pause. "I've been doing security work, sometimes with a partner, sometimes alone, for the past seven years. I work for an agency headquartered in Denver, though they have branches all over the country. Your father contacted the agency office in Chicago and I got a call that same afternoon giving me the details of the assignment. The next day, I was settled into the cabin in Arkansas, keeping an eye on the one you arrived at the next day."

He'd told her more than she'd expected, but so much less than she wanted to know. Though she told herself she should be content with what he'd given, she couldn't resist asking, "Isn't there someplace you call home? Surely you have at least an apartment somewhere."

Keeping his gaze focused on his meal, he shrugged. "I've got a place in Colorado. A little cabin up in the mountains, similar to the one in Arkansas. I usually go there between assignments, unless there's somewhere else I want to go instead."

"No strings, no ties, no commitments," Lauren murmured. "You go where you want, whenever you want."

"Unless I'm working," he reminded her. "I've never walked away from an unfinished job."

So he was at least capable of making a commitment to his career, if nothing else. Lauren wondered rather wistfully if any woman would ever have a chance of receiving an equal amount of loyalty from him. Would he ever settle down with a home and a family? Had he ever even wanted to do so? But those, of course, were the types of questions she knew she couldn't ask him. Not yet, anyway.

She swallowed a sigh and reached for her empty plate. "I'll clear away the dishes."

"No, you take it easy. I'll get them."

"I'm tired of taking it easy. I don't think I'll have any serious relapses from washing a few plates."

Joe looked vaguely annoyed that she argued with him, but offered a compromise. "I'll wash, you dry."

"Deal."

His mouth quirked at her quick acceptance. "You really must be getting restless if you're this excited over doing dishes."

"I'm not used to so much inactivity," she admitted. "I stay pretty busy at home, with work and my affiliation with professional and civic organizations. It's rare that I have an evening to just relax and do nothing—and that's all I've been doing for the past few days."

"You didn't mention a social life," Joe commented, not looking at her as he efficiently gathered dishes. "Is there some guy back in Chicago who's wondering where the hell you are?"

"There are probably several who wonder where I am," Lauren replied flippantly, then added more soberly, "But no one in particular. I haven't been seriously involved with anyone for a long time."

As though he'd read more into her tone than she'd intended him to hear, Joe flicked her a glance over his shoulder as he carried dishes to the sink. "But you were seriously involved?"

"Once. It didn't work out."

"How come?"

She noted wryly that for a man who begrudged revealing even the most superficial details about himself, he certainly didn't mind asking personal questions of her! And she kept answering them, anyway, she thought in self-exasperation, even as she said, "I found out he was using me as a way of getting in tight with my father. I don't like being used because of my father. Then . . . or now," she added, her thoughts turning to the grim present.

"Is that why you're so suspicious of anyone who works for your father now?" Joe asked, raising his voice above the sound of water spilling into the sink. "Because of one stupid jerk?"

"I never said that," she hedged.

"You didn't have to. It was written all over your face when you found out who I was working for when I found you."

She found a dish towel in a drawer beside the sink and twisted it between her hands. "I do trust you, Joe. I just won't forget that your first loyalty is to the man who pays your salary. As it should be, of course."

He placed a freshly washed plate in her hands, but didn't release it until she looked up at him. "My first loyalty," he said when their eyes met, "is to the person I'm protecting. You. If your father's orders conflict with my opinion of your best interests, then I follow my own instincts next time. Do you understand that?"

She tried not to be moved by his declaration of loyalty to her, reminding herself again that he was only doing his job. She was touched, anyway. "I understand. Thank you for reassuring me."

He nodded and turned back to the sink. "Just wanted to make that clear," he said gruffly.

A frustrating, infuriating, fascinating man, she thought again, glancing wistfully at his attractive profile from beneath her lashes. Would she ever fully understand him? Could anyone?

An hour later, Lauren found herself pacing from window to window in the airy, minimally furnished cottage, her gaze drawn repeatedly to the sandy beach, where the gulf waves glittered in the waning sun. It would have been too cool to swim even had she been able, but she longed to be outside, her feet sinking in the wet sand as she enjoyed the mild weather and fresh, salty air.

Joe had been reading since they'd finished the dishes, apparently absorbed in a recent Dean Koontz thriller. Lauren was surprised when he set it down with a gusty exhale. "Get a windbreaker."

"I beg your pardon?"

"If you look out the window and sigh one more time, you're liable to hyperventilate. We'll go for a walk. A short one," he added.

Lauren was already halfway to her bedroom, though she took just a moment to ask, "You're sure it's okay?"

"I wouldn't have suggested it if I thought it wasn't okay," he answered impatiently. "Hurry, though. I want to be back inside before dark."

She didn't linger any longer.

The cottage was built on stilts, with a wide wooden deck all around. Lauren drew a deep breath as she stepped out the door. She turned her face toward the rapidly setting sun, letting the stiff breeze toss her hair carelessly around her. Her lips tasted salty when she moistened them. She smiled her pleasure.

Joe watched her with a bemused expression. "I've never seen anyone enjoy being outdoors as much as you apparently do."

Her smile deepened as she headed for the stairs leading down from the deck. "I know. My father always said I was part plant—have to have my sun and fresh air. I can only stay cooped up inside for a few hours at a time before I have to get out or go bonkers."

"Bonkers, huh?"

"Utterly," she assured him.

"So how come you're an accountant? Why didn't you go into forestry or gardening or lifeguarding or something?"

"The hours I spend working indoors only make me appreciate being outside more. And besides, I like working with numbers, too."

"You're just full of contradictions, aren't you?"

She thought of her feelings for him. Attraction mingled with wariness, implicit trust mixed with rational doubt. "You have no idea," she murmured, stepping off the stairway onto the sand-and-broken-shell beach.

Joe paused for a moment on the lower step, looking at her as if in question, then followed her toward the water.

It was too early in the season for the tourists who frequented Galveston Island in the summers. Lauren spotted only one other person on the beach, a fisherman several hundred yards away, identifiable only as a middle-aged male. She ignored him, turning instead to laugh at a sea gull that hovered above her, squawking a shameless appeal for any treat she might have to offer it. "You're out of luck, bird. I'll bring you a treat next time."

Joe had been watching the fisherman, though he glanced at Lauren when she spoke. "Sea gulls have no pride. They'd stand on their heads for food, if they could."

Lauren chuckled at the dry comment. "True. Last time I picnicked on a beach, there were so many feathered beggars, I kept thinking of Hitchcock's *The Birds*. I was almost afraid not to feed them, in case they got violent."

"You'd never see a cat begging like that. Cats have dignity. They might demand food, but they'd never beg for it."

"You like cats?" she asked, surprised. "Most of the guys I know prefer dogs."

Joe shook his head. He wasn't smiling, exactly, but his light eyes were gleaming with humor. Lauren had to force herself to concentrate on what he was saying rather than how good he looked with the breeze ruffling his gold-tipped hair and the orange sun adding a bronze cast to his already-tanned skin. Had she not been so painfully aware of the gun stuck in the back waistband of his jeans, beneath his navy blue windbreaker, she would have thought he looked like a carefree young beach bum.

"I like cats," he said, apparently feeling no need to defend his preference. "I might even get one of my own someday. A big yellow one, like that one in the cat food commercials on TV."

Lauren slowly shook her head, baffled by this man whose only ambition in life seemed to be to one day own a big yellow cat. Was that his idea of making a commitment eventually, to get a pet?

She walked to the water's edge, letting an incoming wave almost touch the toe of her sneaker. And then the wave receded, leaving wet sand and bits of shell behind it. She picked up an interesting-looking shell, then laughed when she turned it over to find long, hairy legs frantically folding inside it. "Look, Joe. A hermit crab."

He stepped close to look over her shoulder. "Ugly things, aren't they?"

She smiled and turned the shell over again, admiring the delicate pastels swirled into the surface of the crab's adopted home. "They have their own kind of beauty, if you look closely enough. You just have to learn to appreciate it."

Joe's face was so close to hers she could almost feel his breath on her cheek. He surprised her by stroking one blunt finger down the line of her jaw. "I know how to appreciate beauty," he murmured. "And sometimes I don't have to look very hard at all to find it."

She didn't know what to say. It seemed so out of character for Joe to say something like that, which only proved that she really didn't know him at all. But, oh, how she wanted to!

Their eyes held for a long, taut moment. Only inches separated them, their mouths so close that she had only to go onto tiptoes to bring them together. She had to make an effort to keep her feet planted firmly in the sand.

Joe was the one who stepped back first, his head turning away from her to hide his expression as he scanned the beach. "It's getting dark. We'd better go back inside."

A tickling on her palm made her realize she'd forgotten the crab in her hand. She looked down to find it cautiously emerging from the shell, tentatively exploring its surroundings. With care, she bent to place it on the sand, watching it scuttle gratefully into the next incoming wave.

And then she straightened and turned back toward the cottage, avoiding Joe's gaze. "All right," she said. "I'm ready to go in."

Neither of them spoke again as they climbed the stairs to the cottage. Lauren was too busy reminding herself that she wanted to come out of this mess intact—and that included her heart.

Chapter Six

Long after Lauren went to bed that night, Joe prowled restlessly around the living room of the cottage. Barefoot and shirtless, wearing only a pair of worn-soft jeans, he'd spent the past hour berating himself for that momentary loss of professionalism on the beach. He knew better. He just hadn't been able to help himself.

Lauren Caldwell was getting to him. One would think he'd be more cautious, particularly since Ryan's all-too-close brush with death after getting too personally involved during a case. How many times since then had they reminded each other that hormones and handguns just didn't mix?

Knowing he needed rest if he was going to be worth a damn the next day, he finally stretched out on the couch, his weapon close at hand, senses alert even as he dozed.

He didn't know how long he'd been asleep when he was brought instantly, heart-poundingly awake by a resounding crash. He was off the couch in an instant, gun in hand, breath held as he threw himself in the direction of the sound.

He felt like an idiot when he found the loose hurricane shutter banging against the wall in the stiff gulf breeze that had kicked up during the night. Muttering imprecations at his unusual jumpiness, he went outside to secure the shutter. It took less than five minutes. He was still grumbling when he stepped back into the cottage—and came face-to-face with Lauren.

Clutching her bathrobe to her throat, her hair tumbled around her face, she asked, "Are you all right? What was that noise?"

The only illumination in the room came from the security lights outside, glowing through the windows and the door still open behind him. Joe kicked the door closed with one bare foot, deepening the shadows around them, increasing the intimacy. Even in the near darkness, he could see her face, pale and flawless; her eyes, large and luminous; her mouth, soft and vulnerable.

Her mouth. He'd never wanted to kiss any other woman the way he ached to taste Lauren. He was slowly going out of his mind.

"Joe?"

Her voice roused him, made him aware of how long he'd been standing there in silence, staring at her. "Yeah?"

"What is it? What's wrong?"

Ah, hell. Without giving himself time to think about it, he reached for her.

Lauren went stiff when he took her into his arms. As his mouth covered hers, Joe hoped her reaction was due to surprise rather than resistance. He was intensely relieved when her arms went suddenly around his neck, her mouth opening eagerly for his. Groaning deep in his chest, he gratefully accepted the silent invitation, deepening the kiss even as he pulled her closer against him.

He hadn't planned the explosive embrace, but it didn't really surprise him, either. This had been building between them from the beginning, despite both their efforts. Nothing had ever felt so inevitable—or so very right.

She fit into his arms as though she'd been tailor-made for him. Her body was slim and lithe, her mouth soft and sweet. No woman had ever taken him so close to the edge, so quickly.

He wanted her so badly he hurt. The extent of that pain gave him the strength to finally draw away from her.

"You'd better go back to bed," he said, his voice raw, his unsteady hands shoved into the pockets of his now-too-tight jeans.

Lauren made an obvious attempt to pull herself together. "That noise I heard earlier?"

"It was nothing. A loose shutter. Go back to bed, Lauren." He'd meant it to sound like an order, but knew as he spoke that it was much too close to a plea. She looked so dazed and tousled, so damned sexy. He wasn't sure he could stay in the room with her much longer without doing something they'd both probably regret in the morning.

As though sensing his willpower was much too close to the edge, Lauren turned and all but ran to her bedroom. He wondered if she was running from her own needs as much as from his. And he wondered why it mattered so much that she was.

He'd never understood how Ryan could have allowed a woman to distract him so thoroughly from the job he'd been sent to do two years ago. Now he thought he knew. Had Ryan felt this way about the woman he'd become involved with during that assignment? If so, it was no wonder that his own safety had been the furthest thing from his mind. It was no wonder he'd been willing to die for her. Joe was feeling very much that same way now.

He only hoped his own tangled emotions wouldn't lead so close to disaster, as Ryan's had two years earlier. This time Lauren's life could be at stake, as well as his own.

Lauren spent a long time getting dressed the next morning, lingering in the shower, fussing with her clothing, hair and makeup—anything to delay facing Joe for just a little while longer.

Standing in front of the mirror in her bedroom, she noted with relief that the bruises were fading from her face, the swelling gone. Even her arm felt almost back to normal. Had it not been for the dark circles beneath her eyes that she'd so carefully concealed with cosmetics, she'd look just like she always did.

She hadn't slept a wink after Joe had kissed her. Had Joe, too, spent the long hours of dawn awake, aching with frustration and wondering what in the world was going on between them? Or had the kiss been no big deal to him, just a fleeting embrace brought on by adrenaline and proximity?

Could Joe possibly be as worried as she was about where they'd go from here?

When she found herself contemplating changing clothes just to stall a few minutes longer, she realized that she was being an idiot. She couldn't hide in her room any longer. Her floral knit tunic and coordinating blue leggings looked fine. It was time to face Joe.

She found him talking on the telephone in the kitchen. Uncertain whether to enter or give him privacy, she hesitated in the doorway, unable to avoid hearing his side of the conversation. When she heard her own name, she decided to stay.

"The two guys who tried to snatch Lauren," Joe was saying. "Any leads on them?"

She held her breath as he paused a moment, then released it in a disappointed sigh when he muttered, "Damn. How could they have just dropped out of sight like that? Where the hell are they?"

So the men were still at large. Still out there somewhere, maybe looking for her. She shivered and wrapped her arms around her waist in an unconsciously protective gesture.

"I'll be on alert," Joe assured whoever was on the other end of the line. "Caldwell guaranteed me no one could possibly know where we are, but he thought that the last time, too. We still don't know how they tracked her down there."

He was silent for another few moments while the other person spoke. And then he apparently changed the subject. "What have you heard from Ryan?"

Lauren watched as his shoulders suddenly went stiff. "What the hell do you mean, you haven't heard from him? He was supposed to check in yesterday, wasn't he? Has anyone tried to contact him?"

He muttered an expletive, then barked into the phone, "I want to be notified as soon as you hear anything from him, or when you get any information about the two guys who are after Lauren. Got that?"

He hung up a moment later, spotting Lauren in the doorway as he did so. He made a visible effort to smooth his deep scowl. "Morning."

She didn't bother with niceties. "Are we in any danger here?"

"Not as far as I know," he answered with a shrug of one T-shirt-clad shoulder. "The men who attacked you are still at large, but there's no reason to believe they're anywhere around here."

"Who is Ryan?"

His jaw twitched when he answered, "My partner."

"Oh." She cocked her head, studying the expression in his eyes. "You sounded worried when you asked about him."

"He's on an assignment that could be dangerous, and he didn't check in when he was supposed to. I am a little concerned about him."

"You must be close to him," she remarked sympathetically.

"We've been together a long time." As though figuratively closing a door between them, he stood and turned away, opening the refrigerator. "Eggs okay for breakfast? It's either that or frozen waffles."

"I'm not very hungry this morning. I think I'll just have coffee for now."

"At least have some juice with it."

She nodded reluctantly, not wanting to argue with him quite yet. "If you insist."

As she poured her juice, she wondered just how long it would take for her to go stark, raving bananas locked in this cabin with Joe in this mood. She didn't understand him at all. After kissing her half-senseless during the night, he was treating her like a distant stranger this morning, one he didn't even seem to like very much.

She'd give herself an hour before she ran screaming through the cottage. And wouldn't *that* give Joe something to worry about?

"Why don't we do some sight-seeing today?" she suggested impulsively, desperately wanting to be out, away from the awkward tension hovering between her and Joe. "I've never been to Galveston before. I'd love to see the island."

"We're not here for sight-seeing. You'll be safer inside the cottage than out on the streets."

Her fingers tightened around her coffee cup, but she kept her voice steady and cordial. "I know we're not here for sight-seeing, but it still wouldn't hurt to get out some. After all, it's not like anyone's trying to assassinate me or anything. They just want to hold me for leverage against my father. And with you at my side, they won't have an opportunity to get to me, right?"

He seemed to consider her words a minute, then shook his head. "Still too risky. We'll stay in."

Her already-frayed temper snapped. She slapped a hand on the table, making the coffee slosh perilously close to the rim of her cup and the orange juice splash against the sides of her glass. "The hell we will! What gives you the right to tell me whether I can leave this cottage or not?"

Joe's eyes narrowed, but that was his only reaction to her outburst. "I'm being paid to protect you," he said evenly. "I'll do that as I judge best."

"You're being paid by my father, not by me," she reminded him, shoving her chair back so she could stand. "Both of you seem to have forgotten that I'm an adult, fully capable of taking care of myself, if necessary. I'm leaving here in half an hour. If you want to earn your pay, I suggest you be ready to accompany me."

He rose very slowly to loom over her, his eyes snapping with tiny, livid flames deep in their crystal blue depths. "I warned you before about treating me like a servant."

He was angry, and Lauren felt her bravado waver for a moment in the face of that intimidating temper. Still, she preferred him furious to coolly distant. She lifted her chin and stood her ground. "And I warned you about treating me like a helpless child."

Impasse. They stood toe-to-toe, locked in a silent battle of wills. Lauren resisted an urge to cross her fingers, knowing there would be little she could do if Joe refused to yield. She'd be an idiot to leave the cottage alone, and both of them knew it. But damned if she'd sit meekly back like a good little girl while Joe and her father planned every detail of her life, no matter how temporarily.

If nothing else, she'd make Joe feel as though he'd earned every penny of whatever her father was paying him.

She was equally torn between surprise and relief when Joe finally exhaled loudly, shoved a hand through his hair, and gave in. "All right. We'll leave in half an hour."

Not quite sure she'd heard him correctly, she eyed him closely as she asked, "We're going sight-seeing?"

"That's what you want, isn't it?"

"Yes."

"Then we'll go. But," he added in a tone that brooked no debate, "you'll do what I say, when I say to do it, you got that? If I see any reason to be concerned about your safety, we're getting out. No questions. No arguments. Clear?"

"Clear," she assured him, annoyed, but deciding to take what she could get. "I'll go get my shoes."

"I hope to hell they're running shoes," Joe muttered.

Lauren ignored him.

Joe was Lauren's stoic shadow as she strolled leisurely down the historic Strand, investigating every shop and gallery along the way. She clutched a handful of tourist brochures she'd picked up at the Strand Visitors' Center and every few minutes she'd read to him from them, though he showed little interest in her commentary.

"Did you know Galveston Island was once the home of the Karankawa Indian tribe, until the pirate Jean Laffite established the earliest settlement in 1817?"

"No."

"Did you know the Strand was once called the 'Wall Street of the Southwest'? It's considered one of the finest concentrations of 19th-century iron-front commercial buildings in the nation."

"Mmm." Joe kept his gaze moving from side to side as they made their way through a small crowd lining the shop windows.

Lauren knew he wasn't admiring the architecture, but watching for anyone suspicious along their route. She determinedly continued as his tour guide. "The original gaslights have been restored and readapted. Aren't they interesting? Every December they decorate for Dickens On The Strand, a Christmas festival. I'd bet that's really beautiful, wouldn't you?"

"Mmm."

"Oh, look at the horse-drawn carriages! Wouldn't you love to ride in one?"

"Not particularly."

She thought about hitting him. She decided, instead, to enter an old-fashioned candy factory, where the scent of fresh-made fudge soothed her thinning patience.

A while later, a bag of fudge and old-fashioned hard candy added to the stack of tourist brochures, she emerged from the candy shop with Joe close at her heels. Too close, she decided, suppressing a shiver when his arm brushed hers. She stepped quickly away.

"I'd like to tour some of the historic homes," she said in a voice that was all too breathless for her satisfaction. "I love authentic Victorian architecture and these are supposed to be some of the finest examples. The Bishop's

Palace, Ashton Villa, the Moody Mansion. They were all built between 1859 and the turn of the century.''

Looking supremely martyred, Joe nodded. ''Just give me the directions,'' he ordered, pulling the car keys out of his jeans' pocket.

Lauren swallowed what would have been a sarcastic snap about his lack of enthusiasm. She was determined not to quarrel with him during this outing, even if it meant biting her tongue until it bled!

Joe showed some interest in the breathtaking old homes they toured. Lauren caught him looking very closely at the gorgeous woodwork of the rosewood, satinwood and mahogany grand staircase in the entryway of the luxurious Bishop's Palace. Even he seemed rather fascinated by the ostentatious displays of wealth by the original owners of these showcase homes.

''Can't you just imagine the fabulous parties that must have been thrown here?'' Lauren enthused in the forty-two room Moody Mansion. ''All the ladies in their silks and laces and diamonds, and the men in black tie?''

''And the servants living in those dark little quarters provided them, getting by on the ridiculously low pittances they probably received for their work? The five thousand-plus people who died in the hurricane of 1900 while these rich people hid out in their massive fortresses?''

Lauren protested, ''But the tour guide said that the wealthy industrial leaders were instrumental in providing assistance and rebuilding the island after the disaster.''

''Mmm.''

Lauren was getting really tired of those macho grunts. She looked at her watch. ''I'm hungry. Let's have lunch somewhere.''

''How about back at the cottage?''

Disregarding his suggestion, she folded her tourist map.
"That shrimp place built out over the water on the seawall looked interesting. Let's try that."

Joe sighed, but didn't argue.

They were seated outdoors on a large wooden deck at
the back of the restaurant, the gulf waves splashing some
fifteen feet below them. Lauren could see the water
through the cracks in the planking beneath her feet. She'd
tied her hair back with a bright blue scarf to keep it from
blowing so much in the constant stiff breeze, but several
strands had escaped and now wafted around her face. Sea
gulls hovered nearby, hoping some diner would toss them
a morsel. Lauren loved the place.

Charmingly garish souvenir shops, also built on stilts
over the gulf, were located on either side of the restaurant. Savoring her crisp fried shrimp, she studied them,
watching the tourists looking through quarter-a-peek tele-
scopes mounted on the observation decks behind the
shops. "I'd like to go into a couple of those shops when we
leave here."

Joe swallowed a fried clam and frowned at her. "Damn
it, Lauren, this isn't a vacation!"

"It's not a funeral, either!" she snapped back at him.
"Would you lighten up, for pete's sake?"

He lifted an eyebrow in response to her cross grumble,
but remained silent for a moment, stirring the coleslaw on
his plate with his fork. Finally he spoke again, without
looking at her. "If you're worried about being alone in the
cottage with me because of what happened last night, you
needn't be. I won't attack you like that again," he promised gruffly.

Her cheeks flaming, Lauren almost choked on a hush
puppy. She took a long swallow of iced tea before saying,

equally stiffly, "I wasn't worried about being alone in the cottage with you."

Not for the reason he'd implied, anyway, she added mentally. It wasn't Joe's willpower she was worried about, but her own. "I just needed to get out awhile. I didn't want another day of sitting around, worrying about a situation I have no control over."

He seemed to think about her words. "I guess I can understand that," he conceded at length.

"Couldn't you try to enjoy our outing . . . just a little?" she asked, hoping she didn't sound as though she were pleading, even though she was.

He had the grace to look a bit guilty. "It hasn't been so bad," he muttered, giving her a quick, apologetic look. "The Strand was interesting. And this food's good."

Cautiously optimistic, she crossed her fingers beneath the table, hoping the rest of the day would be more pleasant than the beginning had been. She hated being at odds with Joe. For some reason, it was very important to her that they get back on companionable terms. "Maybe you'd like to visit the Seaport Museum this afternoon. That sounds like a guy sort of thing."

His mouth quirked in the closest resemblance to a smile she'd seen all morning. "A guy sort of thing?" he repeated.

"Yes. It's the home of the *Elissa*. A late-nineteenth-century sailing ship that's been turned into a museum. They also have slide shows and displays having to do with the early shipping industry around here."

"I do like ships," Joe admitted.

"So you want to go?"

"Sure. Why not?"

She smiled and dug into her pile of shrimp, hopeful that everything would be back to normal between them now.

* * *

Much later that afternoon, Lauren and Joe sat side by side on a bench at the edge of Seawolf Park on Pelican Island, watching the huge ships entering and departing the port area. Schools of sleek silver fish leapt from the water in front of them, and beyond that colorful, automobile-laden ferries moved traffic from Galveston Island to nearby Port Bolivar. There were other people in the park on this beautiful afternoon, strolling through the glass-sided, three-level white pavilion, fishing from the pier, or from the piles of rocks bordering the park, touring the World World II submarine, destroyer escort, navy jet and military vehicles on exhibit there. Children's laughter drifted from the playgrounds scattered around the park.

As far as Lauren was concerned, she and Joe could have been alone on the island. She had no interest in anyone there but him.

He'd relaxed considerably since their talk at lunch, though she knew he was always on alert for any sign of danger to her. She'd enjoyed their tour of the sea museum, for which Joe had displayed an intriguing fascination, and had laughed frequently at his dry comments in the blatantly tacky souvenir shops. He had utterly refused to pedal a fringed bicycle surrey down the seawall, but had agreed to a ride on the ferry before they'd entered Seawolf Park. Now that he'd gotten over the irritability that had apparently been triggered by his early-morning telephone conversation, Lauren found him a charming, entertaining companion.

But then, she had found him fascinating from the moment he'd pulled her out of that flooding stream in Arkansas. Even his moodiness didn't keep her from being irresistibly drawn to him.

Three boys between the approximate ages of ten and four dashed past them, looking so much alike they had to be brothers. The oldest two were pointing excitedly at a Coast Guard cutter visible in the distance, while the youngest looked fascinated by the leaping fish only a few feet out in the water. He stepped closer to the edge of the embankment to watch them, coming much too close to the sharp drop-off of rock for Lauren's comfort.

Before she could say anything, Joe had moved, catching the boy by the shirt as he moved even closer to the edge, and pulling him back to the sidewalk. "Not too close," he warned the startled tot. "You don't want to fall into the water. One of those fish might decide you look like a snack to him."

"You're s'psed to be watching him, Brad," the middle boy said accusingly to his older brother. "Mom's gonna yell if you let him fall in and drown or somethin'."

"Where *is* your mother?" Joe asked casually.

"Back at the pavilion," the oldest boy replied.

"Maybe you'd all better go find her. This edge isn't really safe for a kid as young as your brother."

Brad sighed gustily, but nodded. "Okay. Get Jimmy's hand, Scott. Let's take him back to Mom."

Joe was scowling when he returned to the bench beside Lauren. "It always amazes me the way some parents just turn their kids loose in public places," he grumbled. "This is an island, for crying out loud. Didn't it occur to their mother that it's surrounded by water?"

"I'd never let my children run free like that," Lauren agreed. "I'll probably be an overprotective mother, but I could never take chances with the safety of my children."

"You planning on having kids anytime soon?" Joe asked with a half smile.

She answered more seriously than he'd probably expected. "I'd love to have a family. I just haven't found anyone to start one with yet."

Joe's smile faded. He looked away.

Disarmed by his concern for the little boy, Lauren dared to ask, "What about your own family, Joe? You said you were separated when you were little. Do you remember them?"

"Yeah. Sort of."

"Brothers and sisters?"

"Six."

"Six!"

He shrugged. "That's why they split us up when our folks died. No one wanted to be saddled with seven kids."

"And you haven't seen any of them since?"

"I've kept in contact with one brother," he answered, sounding evasive. "I don't know what happened to the others."

Trying to understand, she turned on the bench to face him. "Haven't you ever tried to find them? Don't you want to see them?"

"Why should I? They're strangers to me now."

"They're family! That's important."

Joe gave her a skeptical look. "Your own relationship with your father is hardly an endorsement for close family ties. Looks to me like I'm better off on my own."

Stung by his words, Lauren answered rather stiffly. "I've been fighting to maintain a relationship with my father for years, no matter how strained that relationship might be. He's all the family I've got, and I'm not going to let go of that easily. As I said, family is important. I'd give anything to know I had brothers and sisters out there somewhere, and I'd do everything in my power to find them if I found out I did. Even if it didn't work out, even if I were disappointed when I found them, at least I'd know I tried."

"That's just what I'd expect from someone as hopelessly naive as you are," Joe commented indulgently.

Lauren gasped her indignation at the remark. "Naive? I am *not* naive. I just—"

He stunned her into silence by brushing his mouth lightly over hers. And then he stood, looking toward the parking lot while she was still frozen in reaction to the kiss. "We'd better head back. I want to check messages."

Following him to the car with uncharacteristic meekness, Lauren tried to decide why he'd kissed her at that particular moment. Would she *ever* understand this man?

Chapter Seven

The sun had set and a full moon glittered on the waves of the gulf. Joe leaned against the deck railing outside the cottage and stared into the dark horizon, lost in his own thoughts. The cottage was quiet, a wedge of light coming through the closed glass door behind him. He assumed Lauren was still sitting where he'd left her after dinner, curled into a chair in the living room, knitting something with the pale blue yarn she'd purchased at a needlework shop on the Strand that morning.

She'd told him she'd learned to knit as a hobby when she'd been a bored young teenager, waiting for her father to come home from his office. At least it gave her something to do now, she'd added, reminding him that she felt confined by the circumstances under which she was being forced to live at present.

He sympathized with her. He could imagine how frustrating it would be to have someone watching one's every move, to have to get permission to do something as outwardly harmless as sight-seeing. Never one to take orders easily himself, he didn't blame Lauren for feeling resentful.

He shouldn't have agreed to the outing today. It had been a foolish risk, had kept them away from the phone when they should have been waiting for news. He simply hadn't been able to resist the plea he'd heard behind her temperamental show of bravado that morning.

He was finding it very hard to deny her anything. And under the present circumstances, that could be dangerous. For both of them.

Grimly, he acknowledged that he'd lost all objectivity on this case, for the first time in his career. The proper thing to do would be to call his superiors, outline the situation and ask to be reassigned, to have someone else sent in to watch over Lauren.

But even as he considered the option, he knew he wouldn't make the call. For one thing, he hated the thought of another operative staying with her night and day, sharing the beach cottage, taking his meals with her. But even more importantly, he knew he couldn't leave her as long as there was any possibility she might be in danger. It might not be professional, but he needed to stay with her, to make sure no one got to her. He was shaken by the depth of his need to protect her. Not to mention his steadily building hunger for her.

No, it wasn't professional. It was a hell of a lot more than that.

He only wished he knew what he was going to do about it.

During the next two days, Lauren found herself sharing quarters with a serious, withdrawn stranger. Any progress they might have made during their sight-seeing outing, which was not repeated, was lost. She desperately wished she understood why.

Joe said little, smiled less. There were times when she thought she spotted glimpses of his former awareness of her in his eyes, but each time, the expression was quickly masked. He was unfailingly polite, always solicitous of her comfort, careful not to disturb her when she read, watched TV or worked on the sweater she was knitting.

She was beginning to fantasize about punching him right in the stomach, just to get his full attention.

She knew that part of the problem was that he still hadn't heard any word from his partner, Ryan. Apparently Ryan was the only person Joe considered a friend, and he worried about losing that friend. Lauren thought of her own best friend, who lived in St. Louis. Had Peggy been told that Lauren was missing? Was she as worried about her as Joe apparently was about his partner? She wished she could call and reassure Peggy that she was all right, but Joe had flatly forbidden any outside calls other than the scrambled conversations with her father.

And that was another problem. The trial had been delayed yet again, drawing out the time she'd be forced to lie low. Marcus still assured her that he had an ironclad case and that she'd be able to return to her own life soon, but she was beginning to worry about her business. She'd taken a couple weeks' vacation before, usually at this time of year, but soon she'd need to get back to work. Her clients wouldn't be able to wait indefinitely for her to settle her personal affairs.

She sighed and picked up a dropped stitch with her knitting needles, knowing her brooding was accomplishing nothing but further depressing her. The sweater she was knitting was progressing nicely. She'd started it without giving a lot of thought to who it was for, though she was honest enough to admit to herself that it would probably fit Joe to a *T*. The yarn was even a very close match to the clear, light blue of his eyes.

"Caldwell, you're such an idiot," she muttered in disgust.

Across the room, Joe had been absorbed in the book he'd been reading for the past few days. At the sound of her voice, he looked up. "What was that?"

"Nothing. Just talking to myself."

"Oh." Holding his place in the book with one finger, he glanced from her to the kitchen doorway. "You need anything? Coffee? Cold drink?"

"No, thanks."

"Getting hungry? I could start dinner."

"I'm not getting hungry. And even if I were, I'm fully capable of making my own dinner," she answered, unreasonably irritated at his thoughtfulness. She'd much rather have him chewing her out than treating her like a helpless charge he was baby-sitting.

Joe shrugged and opened his book. Lauren gritted her teeth and forced her attention back to her knitting. The room was very quiet, outwardly serene. Yet Lauren was much too aware of the tension that all but hummed between herself and her bodyguard.

Sometime during the night, Lauren woke to the sound of a noise coming from the living room. Squinting to see through sleep-blurred eyes, she peered at the bedside clock: 2:00 a.m. She had turned in before midnight and she knew Joe had been right behind her. What was he doing up now? Had he heard something suspicious? Was something wrong?

Without stopping to think about it, she rolled upright and reached for her robe.

Joe was standing at the glass door, looking outside. He hadn't turned on any lights, so he was little more than a silhouette against the moonlight coming through the glass. There was just enough light for her to see that he wasn't wearing a shirt. His shoulders gleamed softly in the shadows. Her hands itched to feel that smooth, bare skin. She clenched them tightly in front of her. "Joe? Do you see anything out there?"

He looked around with a frown. "You really shouldn't come charging in here every time you hear a sound. You never know what you'll find."

She shrugged off the warning, more concerned with the grim set of his expression. She stepped closer. "Is something wrong?"

He shook his head. "No. Just making my nightly rounds. Old habit. Go back to bed."

She moistened her lower lip with the tip of her tongue. "I can tell something is bothering you. Would it help to talk about it?"

He stood stiffly, his hands clenched at his sides. "Yeah, something's bothering me. *You,*" he growled, startling her. "And there's only one thing I can think of you can do to help."

She felt her eyes go wide. Was he talking about what she thought he was talking about?

Of course he was. If she hadn't been aware of the growing attraction between them by now, she'd truly be as naive as Joe had accused her of being.

Oh, how she was tempted to reach out to him. Instead, she twisted her hands more tightly together and stammered, "I—I don't think that's a very good idea."

"It's a damned stupid idea," Joe agreed gruffly. "I just wish to hell I could stop thinking about it."

"This—whatever it is—it's only because we're alone, together, the way we have been for the past week," she offered hesitantly, awkwardly. "It's just...circumstances." But even as she made the suggestion, she knew her own feelings had nothing to do with proximity or circumstance.

Joe apparently felt the same way. "You think I haven't been in these same 'circumstances' before?" he demanded, sounding irritably impatient. "Well, I have. And I don't get involved with the clients. Ever. Mixing my business with pleasure is a damned good way to end up dead."

Her attention arrested by his haunted tone, Lauren tried to read his face in the shadows. "You sound as though you're speaking from experience."

"My partner got mixed up with a woman on an assignment two years ago. He lost his concentration. Spent several days in a coma and nearly a year of convalescence because of it."

Lauren's hands tightened until her fingers began to ache from lack of circulation. "I'm sorry to hear that. But it has nothing to do with us. After all, we're not, er, involved. And there's no reason we can't keep it that way."

The look he gave her held open skepticism.

"We became friends in that cabin in Arkansas," she said, almost pleading. "Can't we just stay friends?"

He made a thick, incoherent sound and pulled her roughly into his arms. His mouth covered hers before she could utter a protest—even had she thought to do so. The kiss was hard, long, deep. His hands were hungry and near wild as they swept her body, searching out the slender curves beneath the thin bathrobe. His body was hard and quivering against hers.

By the time Joe released her, he was breathing raggedly, his voice raw when he asked, "*Now* do you understand why we can't just stay friends?"

Trembling with need for more of him, she nodded mutely. And then she turned and fled, locking herself into the privacy of her bedroom, where she could fall apart without him seeing her. She spent the rest of the night fighting her desire for this mysterious, unpredictable man, telling herself she would have to be as cautious of him as she was of the hate group that had tried to kidnap her.

Where Joe was concerned, it was her heart that was in danger. And at the moment, that seemed the greater threat to her future happiness.

She talked to her father again the next morning. "How much longer is this going to go on, Dad? You promised you would do your best to wrap it up so I can come home."

Marcus sounded only faintly apologetic. "I know, Lauren. Sorry, but it's taking longer than I expected. The defense keeps coming up with reasons to delay the trial. They know I've got them cold, but they keep hoping they'll find a loophole. They don't have a chance, of course, but we can't blame the defense lawyers for trying. They're good. Just not good enough to win this one," he added, unable to avoid boasting a bit. Marcus had never been shy about singing his own praises.

"How long will the trial take once it gets under way?"

"That's hard to say for sure. A week, two, maybe. Could be longer, depending on how many witnesses are called, how many recesses granted."

"And I'm supposed to put my life on hold for that long?" Lauren demanded, frustration raising her voice an octave. "Dad, I've got a life in Chicago! A career. What about my clients?"

"That's being taken care of."

She frowned. "What do you mean, it's being taken care of? How?"

"I've got one of my accountants taking your calls and handling all the business that can't wait until you return. Your clients have been told that you've been injured in an accident and have arranged for a qualified fill-in until your return. He's implied that you're supervising each account from your convalescence. So far, everyone seems satisfied. You've got a few nice get-well cards waiting for you."

Lauren was as close to a temper tantrum as she'd been since she was twelve. Her father could make her madder than anyone she'd ever known, even when he was supposedly trying to help. It didn't make her feel good to know she could be so easily replaced in her own accounting practice! "How could you do that without even discussing it with me? Didn't you think I should at least be consulted before you arranged something like this?"

Marcus seemed genuinely surprised at her annoyance with him. Which, Lauren thought in exasperation, was exactly the problem. He'd never understood her, never stopped to ask himself what she thought or what she wanted. He only did what he thought best for her, using whatever methods were most expedient for him.

"Never mind," she interrupted his blustering a moment later. "I know you were only trying to help. I just wish you'd talked to me first. Tell your accountant to handle only the most pressing matters, will you? Anything that can wait is to be left for me. I'm serious, Dad. You tell him."

"I'll tell him. He's not trying to take over your practice, Lauren. He's only lending a hand until you get back. Which won't be that much longer," Marcus added confidently, obviously hoping his assurance would appease her.

"I hope you're right."

"You're not having any problems with that bodyguard, are you? I know he's not the easiest guy to get along with, but his superiors told me he was the best they had at this sort of thing. If you want someone else, you just say the word, honey. I'll have someone there before sundown."

"I don't want another bodyguard. I just want my life back."

"I'm doing my best, Lauren."

"So you keep telling me," she murmured with a sigh.

Joe was standing behind her when she hung up. From the look on his face, she could tell he'd overheard the last part of the conversation. "Maybe you *should* ask for another bodyguard," he said quietly.

"But I don't want anyone else," she whispered, and she knew, as Joe probably did, that the words held a double meaning.

His jaw tightened. "It might be best."

"Why?" she challenged him, holding his troubled gaze with her own. "Are you going to let anything happen to me?"

"No," he said instantly, a fire of determination burning in his eyes, in his low, gritty voice. "I'm not going to let anything happen to you. Anyone who wants to get to you is going to have to go through me first."

"Then why would I want anyone else?" she asked.

He stood where he was for a long, silent moment, then gave her a quick, disarmingly crooked smile. "I guess you're right," he said.

He turned and walked away before she could respond to that flash of warmth. She lifted a hand to brush a hair away from her face, and discovered that she was trembling.

It was probably just as well that Joe didn't smile often, she mused dazedly. She simply couldn't trust her reactions when he did.

Joe wasn't sure how much longer he could go on this way. Two more days had passed since Lauren had refused to ask for another bodyguard. Two more days of being with her, wanting her, aching so badly to touch her that he sometimes thought he'd lose his mind. He couldn't even burn off some of the building tension with exercise. He'd have taken several long, hard runs down the beach during the past few days had he not been reluctant to leave Lauren alone for that long.

Ryan still hadn't checked in, and Joe was becoming increasingly worried about him. That, as well as his hunger for Lauren and his frustration at being so close to her, had him edgy and short-tempered.

Lauren, too, had been acting tense and high-strung, jerking as though burned whenever they touched by accident, quickly looking away whenever their eyes met. Joe knew he wasn't the only one fighting the attraction. Knowing she felt it, too, only made it harder to keep his distance.

The trial had finally gotten under way in Chicago, but it was dragging at a snail's pace. It could be weeks before it was over.

Joe couldn't help wondering if he'd still be sane by the end of those weeks.

The explosion came late the next night.

Neither Lauren nor Joe were ready to turn in, yet both

were tired of watching television, reading and knitting. Lauren started to pace. When she realized Joe was pacing, as well, and that they were in danger of colliding whenever their paths crossed, she threw up her hands in exasperation. "This is ridiculous! Let's get outside for a while."

"Are you kidding? It's after midnight."

"And we're both going crazy with cabin fever. Neither of us is going to be able to sleep if we can't relax first. Maybe a walk on the beach will soothe us."

"I don't know..."

She tugged on a sweater to protect her from the cool night breeze coming off the gulf. "I'm going."

"Damn it, Lauren."

She gave him a saccharine smile. "Yes, Joe?"

He muttered a curse. "All right. Give me a minute." He pulled his handgun from the drawer of the end table by the couch and shoved it in the back waistband of his jeans, then shrugged into his navy windbreaker. "That father of yours should have turned you over his knee a few more times when you were a kid," he grumbled, reaching for the door.

Her smile dimmed. "That would have been better than having him gone all the time," she agreed, following him onto the deck.

He didn't respond as he closed the door behind them.

The beach was deserted, most of the cottages within sight completely dark except for outdoor security lighting. The only sounds disturbing the silence were the constant splashing of waves in the gulf and the distant mooing of one of the cows pastured across the highway from the beach area. Bits of broken shell crunched softly beneath their feet as Lauren and Joe walked along the water's edge, heading without spoken intent toward a deserted fishing pier that had long since collapsed into a pile of jutting logs. They didn't speak, though Lauren was aware of every breath Joe took as he walked close beside her.

She stumbled a bit as they topped a waving grass-covered mound of sand just before reaching the old pier. Joe's hand shot out to steady her, and then lingered at her waist. Lauren held her breath, all her concentration centered on that point of contact between them.

Their steps slowed, then stopped. Hidden in shadows, out of sight of the cottages behind them, they turned to face each other. Lauren lifted her face to Joe's, searching his expression in the watery moonlight, studying the deep lines carved around his unsmiling mouth. She could almost see the conflict within him, knew firsthand how he was torn between desire and discretion.

Her own common sense was screaming warnings, reminding her he worked for her father, admonishing her that he was a puzzle, a loner, a man with too many secrets, too many barriers, too many defenses. A man who had offered her nothing—not even his last name.

And yet she wanted him. So badly she ached with it.

How was she supposed to resist a need this powerful, this all-consuming? How was she supposed to turn away from a passion she'd been hoping all her life to find?

Joe brushed a strand of hair from her cheek. She felt the fine trembling in his fingers as she tilted her face into his touch. Her eyelids grew heavy.

His unsteady breath was warm against her skin, his face only inches above hers. "We shouldn't be doing this," he murmured hoarsely.

"No," she whispered, lifting a hand to rest over his heart. Even through his shirt and thin windbreaker, she could feel the rapid pounding, could sense the wildness locked inside him, straining to get out. She wanted to know that part of him, wanted to see what Joe was like when he lost that formidable control of his. Wanted to believe she could release the side of him so few people had probably ever seen.

His head lowered, his lips brushing hers so lightly he hardly made contact. And yet she felt the kiss all the way down to her toes.

"Tell me to stop," he said, his hands sliding slowly around her.

"I wish I could," she responded honestly, her own arms slipping around his neck.

His arms quivered, as though fighting an urge to pull her closer. "Just say stop."

"I can't. I don't want to." She rose on tiptoes to bring her mouth closer to his. "Please, Joe. Kiss me."

He groaned, hesitated only a heartbeat, then crushed her mouth beneath his.

Fully aware of her decision, Lauren opened to him, her tongue eagerly welcoming his, knowing she was initiating a great deal more than a kiss. Maybe it was foolish, maybe it was an open invitation to heartbreak, maybe it was a decision that would change her forever, but for one of the few times in her life, this cautious, responsible accountant was going to take a reckless chance. It felt exhilaratingly liberating to be in charge of her own actions again, at least for this night.

Her arms tightened around Joe's neck when he would have pulled away. "Lauren," he growled, his entire body taut against her, the ridge of his undeniable arousal hard against her abdomen, "if we don't stop now, we won't be stopping at all."

"I don't want to stop," she murmured. "Please. Don't stop."

"Lauren," he moaned, one hand tightening in the back of her hair. "Honey, you don't want this."

"I've never wanted anything more in my life," she corrected him.

His breathing had become tortured, his muscles iron hard with the control he was exerting so fiercely. "I can't make you any promises. I can't give you any flowery words or vows. But I want you," he said roughly. "So badly I can't think of anything else."

"Don't think," she whispered against his lips. "Just feel."

He shuddered and pressed his open mouth to hers, again and again, more and more ardently, his hands sweeping her body, shaping her waist, her hips, her breasts. His back was broad and strong beneath her palms, his arms hard and muscular. His stomach rippled beneath his clothes when she stroked her hands downward from his chest. She wanted to feel him.

His buttons slid easily open to her searching fingers. His flesh was firm and supple beneath the fabric of his shirt. She was glad he didn't have a lot of chest hair. She loved the feel of his sleek, warm skin.

Joe swiftly unbuttoned the chambray shirt she wore beneath her open cardigan. Her bra had a front clasp; he released it with suspicious ease. And then he pushed their clothing out of the way as he brought her against him, pressing her breasts to his chest. He made a choked sound Lauren hardly heard over her own sharp gasp. Her knees went weak.

His mouth against her throat, Joe murmured, "We should go back inside."

"Mmm." Her fingers burrowed into his thick, soft hair as she arched her throat against his wet, open mouth. The cottage seemed so far away.

His lips moved lower, tracing a path from the soft skin behind her ear to the tiny mole just above her right breast. He touched that round dark spot with the tip of his tongue, seemingly intent on exploring her. Lauren shivered as a cool breeze wafted across that damp patch when he moved on.

"Are you cold?" Joe asked, his hand kneading her left breast, his thumb stroking slowly across the hardened nipple.

She gasped. "No. No, I'm not cold."

He sank to his knees in the sand and sparse grass. "Good," he muttered, just before taking the tip of her breast into his mouth.

Lauren's fingers tightened in his hair, her entire body responding to the electrical charge that surged through her as he tugged at her nipple. "Joe!"

He shushed her with a warning murmur before moving to her other breast. She bit her lip to keep from crying out again.

His movements growing more feverish, more impatient, Joe jerked off his windbreaker and shirt and spread them on the thin grass behind her. And then he lowered her carefully backward, following her down. A lump dug into her back through his thin shirt—a shell, a clump of sand, she didn't know which and didn't care.

The brisk wind carried a fine spray of salt that flavored Joe's kisses. She licked his lips, making him groan and surge restlessly against her. Their denim-covered legs tangled, their hips moving in a rhythmic simulation of the lovemaking they both craved.

Endless waves surged within inches of where they lay, and soft moonlight gleamed against their exposed skin. The evening was pure romance, and Lauren reveled in it. She'd never experienced anything like it, wasn't sure she ever would again. She intended to savor every glorious minute.

She didn't think of her recent brush with disaster as he opened her jeans and tugged the soft denim down her thighs. She didn't remind herself that she'd known this man only eleven days. She didn't consider the possibility that anyone or anything would disturb them now. This place, this moment, these were theirs, and Lauren clung stubbornly to the illusion that they were the only two people within miles of this dark, quiet beach.

Murmuring apologies for crushing her, Joe squirmed around to reach into the back pocket of his jeans. He froze a moment, then pulled his handgun from his waistband, setting it on the sand within easy reach, giving Lauren a look of apology as he did so. He then pulled a foil square out of his pocket, his expression endearingly sheepish. "I thought it best to be prepared," he explained. "You've blown my willpower all to hell."

She smiled and pulled his head down to hers. "I'm glad," she murmured, kissing him deeply.

"God, Lauren. I hope you don't regret this," he groaned when he lifted his head.

"No," she promised, confident that no matter what happened, no matter how deeply she was hurt when this was over, she could never regret this magical night in the moonlight. "Make love with me, Joe."

He reached down to the snap of his jeans.

Conscious of the need for discretion, Lauren had to bite her lip again to stifle a wild cry of pleasure when Joe surged into her. She wrapped her legs around his, her exposed skin sensuously abraded by the heavy denim of the jeans he still wore. Her fingers clenched into his bare shoulders, her head tossing restlessly against his spread shirt. She lifted to his thrusts, his breathing harsh in her ear, his name trembling on her lips. And then she gasped as the pleasure became almost too intense to bear.

Forgetting anything but the sensations exploding within her, she bowed upward and shuddered with the force of her climax. Joe swiftly covered her mouth with his own, swallowing her startled cries. And then he, too, stiffened and made a strangled sound from deep in his chest. She thought he might have said her name. She held him closer, sheltering him in her arms until the spasms had passed.

I love him, she thought, staring dazedly up at the star-studded sky. *Heaven help me, I've fallen in love with him.*

And she didn't even know his last name.

Not smart, Lauren. Not smart, at all.

But it seemed now as though this had been inevitable from the moment he'd rescued her from that flooding stream.

Chapter Eight

Joe returned to reality somewhere between one gasping breath and the next. Cursing himself for losing all semblance of discretion or professionalism, he hustled Lauren into her clothes and back inside almost before she could speak. He really had blown it this time, he told himself, double-checking the locks as they entered the cottage. He'd been so deeply absorbed in Lauren that an earthquake couldn't have claimed his attention, much less a couple of armed kidnappers.

She deserved better than him, he thought grimly. As a bodyguard—and a lover.

She was watching him closely, apparently trying to judge his mood. She offered a tentative smile when their eyes met. "I could use a shower," she said, obviously striving to sound glib. "I have sand in places I don't even want to think about."

He motioned toward the hallway. "Go ahead. I'll fix us something hot to drink."

She twisted her hands in front of her, the only sign of her nervousness. Her smile trembled, then steadied. "You could always share the shower with me," she suggested after only the slightest hesitation. "Just in case there are spots neither of us can reach alone."

Joe shoved his hands into his pockets to keep himself from reaching for her. Or was he trying to hide their trembling? "I think we could both use some coffee," he said, trying to keep his voice gentle so he wouldn't embarrass her or make her feel rejected. "It'll be ready by the time you finish your shower."

Her lashes fell, hiding her expression. She nodded. "All right. I won't be long."

"Take your time."

She turned and left the room. Joe stared after her, regretting the way her smile had dimmed, thinking of how much courage it must have taken her to invite him into her shower when he'd been acting so distant since he'd all but attacked her on the beach.

He really was a jerk.

She deserved better.

He took a step toward the kitchen, intent on starting the coffee he'd promised her. And then he stopped, looking back toward the hallway. Another step toward the kitchen, and another full stop. And then he gave a disgusted snort and slammed his right fist into his left palm, his angry curse heating the air around him.

Her wet hair streaming down her bare back, Lauren had her face turned into the water when he slid open the glass shower door. Water beading on her eyelashes, she blinked in surprise as he stepped in to join her, sliding the door closed behind him.

"I decided I might need help getting all that sand off, after all," he told her, forcing himself to smile, though the sight of her wet, nude body had his mouth going dry, his knees weak.

One hand braced against the blue tile wall, Lauren took a slow, all-inclusive survey from his head to his toes, her attention lingering for a moment on the arousal he couldn't have hidden had he tried. Aware that this was the first time she'd actually seen him without any clothing, Joe felt his cheeks warm, to his disgust. Lauren's eyes held a smile when she looked back up at him. "I don't see any sand," she said.

He watched a stream of water cascade over her shoulder to trickle from one soft, perfect breast. His voice was hoarse when he suggested, "Maybe you need to look closer."

"Maybe I do," she agreed, suddenly sounding breathless. "Come here."

He didn't waste any time complying.

They never got around to drinking the coffee.

Her head cradled in the hollow of Joe's warm bare shoulder, Lauren stroked one hand down his chest, feeling his heartbeat slowly steadying after their latest bout of lovemaking. "What time is it?" she asked, her voice husky in the quiet of his bedroom.

He turned his head to look at the luminous digital clock on the nightstand. "Nearly 3:00 a.m."

"Odd. I'm not at all sleepy."

"You should be. You've certainly expended enough energy." He sounded faintly amused.

Lauren was pleased that he seemed to have finally stopped fighting what was happening between them tonight. His well-honed muscles were still and relaxed beneath her hands, his voice deep, lazy and contented. She liked knowing she had put him in this good mood. "Are you tired?" she asked.

"Tired, yes. Sleepy, no."

"Mmm. Maybe we could talk a while, just until we get sleepy."

"Talk about what?"

It was a calculated risk, but now seemed as good a time as any. "Tell me what you remember about your brothers and sisters."

Sure enough, he stiffened, though not as much as she might have expected. "Why?"

"I just want to know. I always dreamed of having brothers and sisters of my own. I can't help wondering if you ever think of yours."

"It's easier not to," he admitted.

She glanced up at him, and something in his eyes made her heart twist in her chest. "Does it hurt so badly to remember?"

He shrugged beneath her. "Not anymore. It did when I was younger, but I got over it."

She didn't believe him for a minute. Some things one never got over. And some things were better brought out into the open than kept bottled up inside. "How old were you when your parents died?"

"Five. They went within a year of each other."

"And that's when you were separated from your siblings?"

"Yeah. I was five. Almost six."

"Do you remember them at all?"

"I remember them."

"What were their names?" She held her breath, waiting to see if he'd answer.

It took him a minute, but he finally replied, with audible reluctance. "Jared, the firstborn. He was eleven or twelve when we were separated. I really looked up to him. Layla, my oldest sister, took care of us most of the time—our little mother. Next was Miles, who always teased us younger ones and made us laugh. Shelley was a cute, curly headed toddler last time I saw her. And Lindsay, the baby. She was less than a year old when they took her. Hadn't had a chance to develop much of a personality yet."

Lauren frowned as she made a quick mental count. "That's only five children. Shouldn't there be one more?"

"Oh, yeah." There was an odd note to his voice she couldn't quite interpret as he continued. "Uh, Bobby. My other brother's name was Bobby."

"You said you stayed in contact with one brother?"

"Bobby. We stayed in the same foster homes until we—until I was sixteen. We hated the foster system, maybe because we didn't give it a fair chance, maybe because we really ended up in some lousy ones. We, uh, I started running away when I was nine. Kept getting caught and brought back. When I left again at sixteen, they either never found me or they'd just gotten tired of looking. Been on my own ever since."

Sixteen. So very young to be on his own. So young to have to learn to depend on no one but himself. No wonder he'd become so much of a loner since. It was the only life he'd ever known. "Where is Bobby now?"

"I don't know." His expression had gone distant again, his voice grim. She could feel him withdrawing from her once more.

Quickly she changed the subject, determined not to ruin this night together. "How did you get into the bodyguard business? You said you'd been in it seven years. You were very young, weren't you?''

"Do you remember everything I've ever said to you?" He sounded partly amused, partly exasperated.

At least that was better than the distance he'd almost put between them, she decided in relief. "Yes."

He shook his head against the pillow. "Why are you so curious about me?"

She blinked. "*Shouldn't* I be?" she asked pointedly, making a vague gesture with one hand to indicate their intimate position.

He cleared his throat. "Oh."

She wondered again if he ever allowed any woman close enough to really know him. Or had all his encounters been brief, meaningless, anonymous? If so, how very sad.

"Well?" she prodded, trying to redirect her own thoughts. She didn't like thinking of Joe with other women.

He gave an exaggerated sigh, but answered. "I don't really know how I ended up in this business. I was looking for work, applied at a security agency in Denver, and almost before I knew it, I'd been given an assignment. I showed an aptitude for security work, so I've made out all right at it."

"The right place at the right time, is that it?"

"You could say that."

"Do you like your work?"

"I haven't had many complaints."

"Have you ever been in real danger?"

"A time or two."

"Have you ever been hurt?"

"I was shot in the thigh once. Took the edge of a knife down my rib cage. Broke an arm. Nothing serious."

Her breath had lodged somewhere in her throat. She released it with a gasp. "Nothing serious!" She rose on one elbow to examine the long, thin scar on his rib cage that she'd first noticed in the shower. She hadn't commented on it then. Now that she knew what had caused it, she felt rather sick. The round, puckered scar on his left thigh didn't make her feel any better. A bullet wound. "You could have been killed."

He shrugged. "All part of the job."

"Maybe you should consider finding another job," she suggested shakily, shuddering as she thought of him wounded and bleeding.

"I've been considering that a lot lately," he replied, and his voice had turned sober again. "I seem to have lost my edge."

She bit her lip. "You're not saying that because of what's happened between us, are you?"

"I'd say that's a damned good example." His self-censure was evident. "I've never gotten personally involved in a case. I've never lost my objectivity—before now."

She wanted to suggest that maybe what they had was special, that maybe it was too powerful, too rare to resist. She knew it had been for her. She didn't quite have the nerve to tell him so, yet. She had no way of knowing whether Joe's feelings were as strong as her own, though she took some comfort in knowing this wasn't something he took lightly. "I'm not worried about your competence," she assured him instead. "I feel utterly safe with you."

"I hope you're right," he muttered, his arm tightening rather convulsively around her shoulders. "All I can say is that someone would have to kill me to get to you."

Her own fingers tightened on his shoulder in a futile gesture of protection. "It won't come to that." *Please, don't ever let it come to that.*

She wanted to distract them both from thoughts along that line. "Tell me about your partner."

"Ryan? What do you want to know?"

"How old is he?"

"A little younger than I am."

"How old are you?" she asked, suddenly realizing she didn't know.

"I'll be thirty soon."

"When?"

"Soon."

She frowned at his habitual evasiveness, but asked, instead, "What's Ryan like? All serious and obsessively cautious, like you?" she added, trying to tease him into a lighter mood.

Joe made a quiet sound that could have been a swallowed chuckle. "Hardly. Ryan's too reckless for his own good. Life's just a long chess match to him, and he's always in check, one step away from disaster. Yet somehow he always comes out the winner—so far, at least," he added, a note of worry creeping into his voice.

"You'll hear from him soon," Lauren assured him.

"How do you know?"

"I just do."

"Psychic, are you?"

"Optimistic," she corrected. "I never give up hope that everything will turn out for the best. This trial will be over soon, the creeps who tried to kidnap me will be captured and jailed, your partner will show up safe and sound, my father and I will finally start to communicate."

And you'll learn to love me the way I love you. If I'm going to dream, I might as well dream big.

"You're a dreamer," Joe accused her mildly, as though he'd read her thoughts. Lauren sincerely hoped that was one talent her enigmatic bodyguard didn't have.

"Maybe."

"Definitely. But sweet," he added unexpectedly, giving her a rough hug that brought a lump to her throat. And then he yawned. "I guess I am getting sleepy, after all."

His yawn triggered her own. "Me, too."

He tucked her more snugly into his shoulder. "Go to sleep, Lauren. We can always play Twenty Questions tomorrow."

She smiled and closed her eyes. At least they had tomorrow, she thought as she allowed her thoughts to drift. She only wished she could be as confident about the days beyond that.

As he would have expected, Lauren was sleeping deeply when Joe awoke at his usual time, 7:00 a.m. He lay still for several long moments, watching her sleep, noting the faint purple smudges tinting the almost translucent skin beneath her long, dark lashes. She needed her rest.

He slipped from the bed, gently pulling the coverlet over her bare shoulders. She murmured something in her sleep and burrowed more deeply into the pillow. His throat was unaccountably tight when he made himself turn and walk away.

While he made coffee, Joe looked out the window over the kitchen sink. It was a gloomy morning, the clouds hanging low and gray over the gulf, sheets of rain sweeping the deserted beach. He couldn't help thinking of the night he'd found Lauren in the rain—just short of two weeks ago.

He poured himself a cup of coffee, then turned on the radio built into the wall to counteract the stark silence of

the morning. "Woke up in love with you," a cheery voice
sang out. "Oh, what a beautiful day."

Joe choked on a scalding sip of coffee and hit the power
button again. Maybe he didn't want to hear the radio, after all.

There were a lot of things he could be doing. Starting
breakfast. Washing a load of underwear. Calling in for
word of Ryan. Trying to decide what to do with the rest of
his life.

Unfortunately, the only thing he seemed able to do this
morning was to stand around the kitchen, sipping coffee,
watching the rain, and reliving the night in Lauren's arms.

He really was in trouble this time, he thought grimly.

Big-time trouble.

It was after ten when Lauren woke. The first sound she
heard was the rain against the windows. She shivered at the
memories that sound evoked and opened her eyes to look
for Joe.

She was alone in his bedroom. The bed was cold beside
her. She decided to take a shower before going in search of
him. She needed the time to prepare for whatever mood he
might be in today.

Showered and dressed in a brightly colored nylon running suit over a hot-pink T-shirt, she finally decided she
was ready for him. She'd half expected to find him in the
kitchen. Though she found evidence of him there in the
half-full pot of coffee and the used cup beside it, the room
was empty. Nor was he in the living room. Frowning, she
wondered where he'd gone.

And then a movement caught from the corner of her eye
made her look out the glass door and cock her head in
question. Joe stood outside on the deck, leaning against
the railing. He wore nothing but a pair of jeans, and was

apparently oblivious to the light rain soaking him to the skin. His hair was plastered to his head, and rivulets of water ran down his bare arms and shoulders. He stared out toward the gulf, seemingly watching a trawler chugging its way across the horizon.

"What in the . . . ?" She opened the door, staying inside where it was dry. "Joe? What are you doing?"

"Taking a shower. Want to join me?"

She stared at him, warily studying the crooked smile he gave her. "You haven't been drinking, have you?"

"Lauren, it isn't even noon yet."

"Yes, I know. Are you aware that it's raining?"

"Yeah, I noticed that. Feels good. It's warm. Sure you don't want to try it?"

She shook her head, trying to figure him out. "You're nuts."

He chuckled. "Haven't you ever taken walks in the rain?"

"Not without an umbrella."

"Then you've definitely been missing out on something," he assured her, and reached out to pull her into his arms.

Before she could sputter a protest, he covered her mouth with his own. Lauren no longer cared that it was raining, or that her freshly washed and dried hair was getting wet again. Lost in the hunger and the magic of Joe's kiss, she wouldn't have cared if a hurricane raged around them. She would have felt as safe and sheltered in his arms as she did now.

Joe was difficult enough to resist even when he was cautious and moody. On the rare times, like this one, when he released his teasing, whimsical side, she was putty in his hands. Her arms locking around his neck, she decided she'd better not let him know that. She was vulnerable enough to him as it was.

"You *are* crazy," she told him when he finally released her mouth. She kept her arms around his neck, her face tilted up to his, blinking raindrops out of her eyes.

He grinned. "I've decided I like seeing you wet. Besides, you sober accountant types need more adventure in your lives."

"Something tells me you're all the adventure I can handle," Lauren assured him with a laugh.

"You can count on that. Want to run down to the beach?"

"I'm barefoot."

"Yeah. Me, too. Soggy shoes are really disgusting."

"There are shells between here and the beach," she pointed out. "Sharp, broken shells. Bloody feet are even more disgusting than soggy shoes."

"True." He looked thoughtful for a moment, then shrugged and swung her up into his arms, her feet dangling several inches above the deck. And then he started walking toward the stairs.

"Joe!" She tightened her arms convulsively around his shoulders. "You can't carry me down those stairs."

"Of course I can," he corrected her. And did.

"But what about *your* feet? Won't they get cut?"

"Calluses," he answered, walking almost as easily across the shells as he would have on plush carpeting.

"Why are your feet callused?"

"From breaking boards and stuff. You can walk now. We've reached the sand." He swung her down, helping her catch her balance as she landed on her feet.

She absently pushed a sodden lock of hair away from her face. "You break boards with your feet?"

"Doesn't everyone? Watch that piece of driftwood. You don't want to stumble over it." He took her hand as he spoke, leading her around the gnarled wood half submerged in the dark sand. His fingers entwined with hers, he started walking, slowly, not taking her far from sight of their cottage.

Lauren realized it was the first time they'd been outside when Joe wasn't armed. He must be feeling more confident about their security. But then again, a man who could break boards with his feet probably didn't even *need* a gun.

"You are a very strange man, Joe Whatever-your-name-is," she informed him gravely.

He gave her a grin that was so damned sexy she fancied it could almost bring steam from her wet skin. "Yeah, probably. How do you like your first walk in the rain without an umbrella?"

His thigh brushed hers as they walked, their steps closely matched. The light, warm rain fell softly over them, running down their arms to trickle from their snugly clasped hands. Lauren sighed in exquisite pleasure. "I love it."

He gave her hand a squeeze. "Good. Let me know if you get chilled."

Chilled? With him so close to her, his bare chest only inches from her lips should she turn his way? Not likely! "I will," she assured him anyway. "Do you do this sort of thing often?"

He shrugged ruefully. "This is really more Ryan's style. He's the impulsive one. I'm usually pretty dull."

"Why do I find that so hard to believe?"

"Beats me." He veered his direction enough to pull her ankle-deep into an incoming wave. She squealed at the water's coldness, then scolded him for getting too close to the waterline. He pointed out that she was already wet, so what was the difference?

"The difference is that the rain's warm and the water is cold," she retorted. "If we both catch pneumonia, then who's going to take care of us, hmm?"

"Your father can nurse us," Joe suggested with a grin.

She giggled at the improbable retort, pleased that he felt comfortable enough now to tease her. "Yeah. Right. He can take shifts with the tooth fairy."

"Works for me." He leaned over to kiss her smile, then straightened and turned back toward the cottage. "We'd better go back in. You haven't even had breakfast yet."

She shivered as a sudden breeze swept her wet skin. "Maybe you're right. Coffee sounds pretty good right now."

She paused on the deck when Joe opened the glass door for her. "We'll track water inside," she fretted.

"It's a beach cottage. It's designed for this sort of thing. Just make a dash for the bedroom and get into some dry things. I'll make a fresh pot of coffee."

She reached out to touch the hard ridge of his jaw. "Come with me and I'll help you dry your back."

His eyes narrowed. "If you do that, it'll be a while before you get your coffee," he warned.

She stroked her thumb slowly over his lower lip. "It'll be a while before I'll want any," she replied.

Moving as quickly as he had the first time, Joe swung her into his arms again. This time she didn't bother to protest being carried. She was starting to enjoy it.

When they finally got around to eating, it was lunchtime. They worked together on a light meal of quiche and salad, and after they ate they stood side by side at the sink to wash dishes. George Strait crooned a love song from the radio, while Lauren and Joe debated the relative merits of Eric Clapton's original recording of "Layla" as opposed to his more recent acoustic version from the "Un-plugged" album. Lauren was delighted that Joe liked music as much as she did. Maybe they had a few things in common, after all, she told herself optimistically.

Since it was still raining steadily outside, she unearthed a Monopoly set from a cabinet in the living room to keep them occupied for a while that afternoon. Though he didn't show a lot of enthusiasm for the game, Joe took his place across the table from her without protest. Before long, his competitive spirit kicked in and he got into the game as intently as Lauren.

She'd been ahead until that point. When she realized she was falling behind, she decided it would be a good idea to distract him, and maybe get a few more of her questions about him answered at the same time. "Would you look for them if you had the chance?" she asked without preamble.

Startled, Joe looked up in question from his contemplation of the playing board. "Look for *who?*"

"Your brothers and sisters," she answered, rolling the dice and moving her playing piece the designated number of spaces. "Do you think you'll ever try to find them?"

"Why should I?" he asked gruffly, taking his own turn at the game. "I don't even know them."

"I think you should try."

Without immediately responding, he took his time reading a Chance card. He frowned, tossed two pastel play-money bills into the bank, then asked, "Why?"

"Because they're your family. And because no one should be as alone as you are. I think you need someone to care about," she added daringly. "Someone other than your friend Ryan."

"What makes you think I'd care about my siblings if I should find them?" he challenged, ignoring her reference to his partner. "They're strangers. It's possible I wouldn't even like the adults they've become."

"That's true. Or maybe you'd love them. Maybe you *still* love them."

"You don't know what you're talking about," he said bluntly, and gestured toward the board as she moved her Scottie dog playing piece to Park Avenue. "That's mine. Pay up."

She counted out the rent with only half her attention. "I know *I'd* look for them if they were my brothers and sisters. Jared and Layla and Lindsay and Miles and, uh..."

"Shelley," he supplied with some reluctance.

"Right. And Bobby," she finished, pleased with herself for remembering most of the names. "How could you not want to know them?"

"I've got enough to do just watching out for my own hide," he muttered. "And yours, at the moment. Roll the dice."

Frowning, she did so, shaking her head when she promptly landed in jail. She produced her Get Out Of Jail Free card with a flourish, then took her courage in her hands again to change the subject with another question. "Have you ever been in love, Joe?"

"I can't concentrate on two games at once," he complained. "What will it be, Monopoly or Twenty Questions?"

"Twenty Questions," she answered promptly, setting down her playing piece.

He scowled. "I figure you've got about three questions left. Go ahead and get them over with."

"Three? How did you come up with that number?"

"I started counting with your first one. I think it was right after I pulled you out of that creek," he said wryly. "Go ahead, ask what you have to."

"All right. *Have* you ever been in love?"

"No."

She blinked at the blunt, utterly certain reply. "Never?"

"Is that another question, or an extension of the same one?"

"An extension. I just wanted to make sure I'd heard correctly."

"You heard correctly. I've never been 'in love.'" He added a rather mocking twist to the phrase. "I've been in heavy lust a few times—"

Like now? she wondered, not at all pleased with the possibility.

"But that's all there was to it," he concluded. "That's all I ever wanted it to be."

"Why?"

Watching her steadily, he shrugged. "Because I'm not the nine-to-five, three-piece-suit, white-picket-fence type. Never had that kind of life, wouldn't know how to go about living it. From what I've seen of so-called traditional family life—from my own to the lousy foster homes I was stuck in—I can't see any reason to willingly walk into that trap."

Lauren had lost all enthusiasm for the board game. A hard lump sat in her chest, just about where her heart would be. If she'd been trying to find reassurance that Joe wouldn't be walking away from her when this "assignment" was over, she'd been bitterly disappointed. He couldn't have made himself more clear about his aversion to commitment.

"You don't think it's possible to have a successful relationship, to build a happy, supportive family?" she felt compelled to ask, anyway.

His mouth twisted. "Do *you?*" he returned pointedly, obviously referring to her own strained relations with her father.

She sighed. "I want to believe it is. I have seen a few examples. My friend Peggy is very happy in her marriage, and her children are being raised with love and security."

"Then they're lucky. And atypical, from what *I've* seen. I'm not saying it can't ever work out, Lauren. I'm just saying I don't think it ever would for me. I just don't know how to go about it—don't know if I even want to try. Do you understand that?" he added, his tone more gentle now, holding just a trace of her own deep regret.

"I guess I do," she whispered, then looked away. "I'm thirsty. Want me to bring you a soft drink when I get one?"

"Yeah, thanks. What about the game?"

She pushed herself to her feet. "I think I've had enough of the game." *Both of them,* she added silently. "You win."

He seemed to hear the unspoken addition, and to agree. "I'll put this away while you're in the kitchen."

She nodded and left the room, her steps lacking their usual spring.

Okay, Lauren, now you've done it, she told herself, staring blindly out the kitchen window to the gray seascape beyond. *You've fallen in love with a man who isn't interested in being loved. Who'll be leaving as soon as he finishes his job and draws his pay for taking care of you. Real smart.*

What are you going to do now?

Chapter Nine

The cellular telephone over which they held their scrambled conversations with the outside world rang several times that afternoon. Joe was left frowning and withdrawn after a talk with his superior in the security agency. When Lauren asked about it, he made a visible effort to smooth his expression and told her he was still worried about his partner.

Marcus then called, to harangue Joe about his daughter's safety, and to boast to Lauren about his brilliant court maneuvers. When she pressed him for reassurance of when she could return to her apartment, he became evasive, reminding her that the trial was a lengthy and complicated one. He then admitted that the defense had just been granted a one-week continuance to prepare some alleged "new evidence."

"It's a load of bull, of course," Marcus added. "Just another delay while they scramble for any lifeline they can find. But it does mean it'll be a bit longer before I'd feel safe about letting you come back home.

"Things should be back to normal soon," he assured her, forestalling her protest. "I've still got people out looking for the two bastards who tried to kidnap you—as well as the police and the feds. They won't be able to evade apprehension much longer. Don't you worry about it, sweetheart. Everything's being taken care of."

"I *am* worried about it, Dad," she snapped, tension making her voice sharper than she'd intended. "I want my life back! I want to be able to go outside without an armed escort! I want to go to sleep without wondering if anyone is going to break in during the night and drag me out of my bed. Is that so difficult for you to understand?"

"Lauren, honey, there's no need to get so upset," Marcus assured her, flustered by her outburst in a way he'd never be disconcerted in the courtroom. "There's no reason to believe anyone is still looking for you. The trial's under way now, and any fool must know that you're under heavy security. They probably took to their heels right after bungling their attempt to grab you. I'm sure you're perfectly safe."

"Then why am I still confined here?" Lauren challenged him. "And why do I still have a full-time bodyguard?"

"It's just a precaution, Lauren. Just to set my mind at ease so I can concentrate on my prosecution. It'll all be over soon."

"I'm so glad. I wouldn't want to interfere with your concentration any longer than absolutely necessary," she answered icily. And then she hung up, knowing how much Marcus hated having anyone but him bring a conversation to an end.

She didn't like it when she lost her temper with her father. Didn't like the bitterness she'd heard in her own voice with her last words to him. But, damn it, she was tired of everyone deciding what was best for her! Tired of putting her own life, her own needs, on hold so that her father wouldn't be inconvenienced by any potential danger to her.

"You okay?"

She looked up to find Joe standing nearby, watching her warily, as though expecting her to burst into tears or start throwing things. She composed her expression and lifted her chin, keeping her voice even. "I'm fine. I just get very frustrated with him at times."

Joe slipped his hands into the back pockets of his jeans, looking a bit uncertain of her mood. He'd been wearing that same expression ever since their frank conversation about commitments and relationships. Lauren wondered if he thought he'd broken her heart. He had, of course, but darned if she'd let him know. She might not have control over her life just now, but she could at least hold on to her pride.

"Is being here really so bad?" he asked finally, nodding toward the cellular telephone to indicate her bitter complaints to her father.

Being here, with Joe, was all too nice, in some ways. Which was one reason she was so worried about how much longer it would last. She was certain that the more time she spent with him, the harder it would be to see him walk away when the time came. "I just don't like being confined, not knowing what's going on with my own life," she commented.

He nodded. His eyes held a frown, though he managed a weak smile for her benefit. "Would it make you feel better to get out for a while?"

"Out?" she repeated, not quite sure what he meant. "Another walk in the rain?"

His smile deepened. "I thought we'd drive this time. Maybe even take an umbrella. I'm out of a few things and need to do some shopping. Afterward, we could have dinner, and we'll let someone else do the cooking and cleaning up this time. We could both use a change of scenery, I think."

"Sounds good to me," she accepted without hesitation. "I'm out of shampoo, myself."

"So what are we waiting for? Let's blow this joint," he drawled, trying to make her smile. He was pleased when he met with success, drawing at least a fleeting smile from her as she turned and hurried toward her bedroom, telling him over her shoulder that she wanted to change her clothing and promising to take only a few minutes to do so.

His own smile faded the moment she was out of sight. It had been a hell of an afternoon. The day had started well enough, both of them feeling playful after their reckless interlude in the rain, the resulting lovemaking eager and passionate.

And then had come that awkward talk about families and commitments—the one that had left Lauren looking uncomfortably disappointed—and then the call from his superior. That call had effectively removed any false security he might have nourished during these past few trouble-free days in Galveston.

When there'd been no sign that anyone had followed them from Arkansas, no indications that he and Lauren had drawn any undue attention during their stay here, no reason to believe they were in danger of any kind, Joe had allowed himself to agree with Marcus that Bullock's followers had given up on their stupid, risky plan to grab Lauren for leverage against the prosecution of their leader.

Now he'd been told that the two suspects in the attempted kidnapping had been spotted by police in Beaumont, Texas, all too close to Galveston for Joe's peace of mind. They hadn't been apprehended, had gotten away after being recognized during a routine traffic violation stop, and no one knew where they were now. But it was safe to assume they were still somewhere in the area.

What the hell were they doing here? How had they known to come here? And how stupid was Joe being to take Lauren out this evening, despite the risk?

He told himself she would be as safe, if not safer, in the public places he'd take her to than she would here, alone with him. He tried to reassure himself that it would be foolish to follow through on his initial urge to get the hell out of Texas without stopping to make plans for their destination and arrangements for safe contact to be made once they'd arrived there.

But even as he considered those excuses, he knew his real motivation for taking her out was because he hadn't cared for the traces of sadness mirrored in her eyes all afternoon, hadn't at all liked hearing her complaints to her father that she felt frustrated and confined being with "a full-time bodyguard," as she'd referred to him. As he'd noted before, it was growing more and more difficult for him to deny Lauren anything, and that was making him increasingly nervous. For several reasons.

She came back into the room, wearing an emerald green silk blouse that deepened the green of her eyes and a short, black skirt that made her legs look long and even more luscious than usual. Her hair was brushed to a sleek, shining, honey-colored curtain to her shoulders, and she'd touched up her makeup with a smoky eye shadow and richly tinted lip gloss. Joe felt his mouth go dry. He was acting like an awkward teenager in the presence of his first major crush, he thought with ironic self-deprecation.

He glanced down at his own clothes. "Maybe I should change."

"You look fine," she assured him with a quick survey of his burgundy cotton shirt and gray twill casual slacks. "I just wanted to wear something other than jeans for a few hours."

He could have told her that she looked as beautiful in her jeans and running suits as other women did in designer gowns and priceless jewels. He almost did tell her, but bit the words back because they made him uncomfortable. Flowery speeches were Ryan's style, not his, despite his few lapses since he'd met Lauren. He shoved his hand in his pocket to pull out the car keys and nodded toward the door, avoiding her eyes. "Okay, let's go," he said gruffly.

Lauren nodded and started for the door. She didn't seem bothered by his lack of gentlemanly courtesy in not even telling her how nice she looked. Maybe, he thought guiltily, because she'd learned not to expect such niceties from him. "Lauren?"

She looked over her shoulder at him. "Yes?"

"You look beautiful."

Her smile was radiant. His chest went tight in reaction. "Thank you," she said softly.

He nodded and reached around her to open the door, careful not to touch her. If he touched her now, they'd never leave the cottage. "Let's go," he said, hoping his desperation wasn't audible to her all-too-perceptive ears.

Lauren wondered at Joe's emotions as he guided the rental car down Seawall Boulevard before turning left on 61st Street. He didn't seem to be in a bad mood, exactly, but neither was he in the frivolous, impulsive mood he'd been in earlier that day, to her surprised delight. He'd hustled her out of the cottage as though escaping a fire, but not before she'd seen the desire in his eyes when he'd so touchingly—and so unexpectedly—told her she was beautiful.

Still, something had changed between them. Had it been a result of that unsettling conversation about commitment, or was Joe still brooding over the telephone call with his superior that had obviously displeased him?

Concentrating on her enigmatic lover, she paid little attention to the passing street signs until he turned left on Broadway. Having expected him to turn right, toward the main part of the island, she glanced through the windshield ahead and asked, "Where are we going?"

"Houston."

Intrigued, she looked back at Joe. "How long will it take to get there?"

"About an hour. I thought you might be ready for a change of scenery."

"Will we be taking another ferry?"

"No. There's a bridge. How about some music?"

So he wasn't in the mood to talk. Lauren suppressed a sigh and obligingly turned on the radio, tuning in a light country channel she thought he'd like. Trisha Yearwood's liquid voice spilled through the speakers. Lauren made no pretense of watching the scenery as they traveled toward Houston. Her attention was all focused on the driver. Joe was so deeply lost in his own thoughts that he didn't even seem to notice she was staring at him.

Just what was going on in that handsome head of his? she wondered gravely. And how, exactly, did she fit into his apparently somber deliberations?

* * *

Joe stopped at the first shopping mall he spotted once they arrived in Houston. They found a variety store inside, where they filled a cart with shampoo, toothpaste, Lauren's favorite moisturizer and Joe's shaving cream. She felt a bit uncomfortable as she added a box of tampons to the cart, knowing she'd be needing them within a few days. Joe didn't seem at all disconcerted when he tossed a box of condoms on top of the growing pile.

Lauren found herself thinking again of how intimately their lives were entwined, considering how briefly they'd known each other. They were living as closely as a married couple, yet there were so many things they didn't know about each other. Little details like Joe's last name, for example, she thought with a wry twist to her mouth.

"Anything else?" Joe asked, glancing at a cosmetics display.

She shook her head. "Dad took care of everything else I needed. His secretary, or whoever arranged to have my things waiting for me, was very efficient."

She noted that Joe suddenly frowned at her words, and wondered what she'd said to disturb him. But then he smoothed his expression and turned the cart toward the checkout stand.

Carrying the plastic shopping bag, Joe followed Lauren back out into the busy mall a few minutes later. "Where to?" he asked.

She glanced around and shrugged. "Is there something else you need?"

"I could use a couple of shirts. I didn't bring many with me. You're probably getting tired of seeing me in the ones I've been rotating. I'm not too good at shopping, want to help me pick out a couple of things?"

Now he was asking her to help him select new shirts. They *were* starting to act like a married couple, Lauren thought with an underlying wistfulness. If only...

"Lauren?" Joe prodded. "D'you mind? I can always get by with what I've got if there's something you'd rather do."

She shook her head, trying to shake off her introspective mood at the same time. Joe was obviously trying to entertain her, the best he knew how. The least she could do was cooperate. She managed a smile. "You should know by now that I love to shop. Let's find a men's store."

She succeeded better than she'd expected in lightening her mood—and Joe's, too, apparently. He even laughed aloud when she teasingly suggested that he try on an incredibly ugly orange and green shirt they discovered in the men's store. "I'd rather be dipped in honey and tied to an anthill than to have anyone see me in that thing," he said with a grin.

"You'd be gorgeous even in this," Lauren assured him, mischievously patting his firm bottom as she spoke, then giggled when his lean cheeks warmed. She just loved making Joe blush, she mused as he quickly looked around to make sure no one had seen her bold behavior. He seemed so much more...attainable when he was rattled, she thought, her smile fading.

They selected two pullovers and a sport shirt, adding a pair of jeans that would go with all of them. And then Lauren spotted a particularly attractive silk tie in shades of navy, gray and burgundy. "This would look nice with the burgundy shirt and gray slacks you have on," she told him.

He picked it up, looked at it a moment, then nodded. "Think you could find a sport coat to match? Size forty, long."

She gave him a questioning look. "You want to buy a sport coat?"

"Yeah. I'll wear it when I take you to dinner tonight."

"Joe, that really isn't necessary. We can go somewhere casual."

"Help me find a jacket, Lauren." It wasn't a request.

Fifteen minutes later, they left the store. Joe carried the two pullovers, the sport shirt and the jeans in a bag bearing the store logo. He wore the tie and jacket.

And he looked spectacular in them, Lauren noted, watching the feminine heads that turned as he walked past. *Lucky you,* those women seemed to say when their eyes met Lauren's. She supposed she was lucky—after all, Joe was hers, for now. She should try to be content with that. Most of the other women admiring him probably would have been.

But Lauren knew even as the thought crossed her mind that she wanted more than these few days with Joe.

Much, much more.

After leaving the mall, Joe drove without hesitation to a trendy restaurant in an upscale Houston neighborhood. Though it was only seven, the restaurant was already crowded. Joe put his name on a list with the receptionist, then guided Lauren into the bar for the thirty-minute wait they'd been told to expect. Joe assured her the food there was worth the wait. He spotted a table for two in a relatively quiet corner of the bar and occupied it quickly, just beating another couple to it. The smile he gave Lauren as they sat down was one of those chest-beating-male types, holding a trace of smugness at his table-hunting prowess.

"What would you like to drink?" he asked as a harried-looking cocktail waitress approached.

Lauren requested white wine, then looked at Joe after he'd placed his own order. "I take it you've spent time in Houston before?" she asked, referring to his ease at finding the mall and this restaurant.

He nodded. "There aren't many places in Texas where I haven't been. I get a lot of assignments in this state. I was born in Texas," he added.

"Really? Where?"

"Texarkana, right on the Arkansas border. I lived there until my parents died."

She'd finally learned not to ask a lot of questions about his past, but to allow him to volunteer bits and pieces along the way, as he just had. Questions only made him withdraw, and that was one thing she really didn't want tonight. Instead she said casually, "I've only been to Texas a few times, shopping in Dallas and a vacation in San Antonio once. Ever taken the River Walk in San Antonio?"

"The Paseo del Rio? Yeah, it's nice."

She wondered who he'd been with. "It's very romantic at night, isn't it?"

"I guess. So, uh, were you there with anyone special?"

"My friend Peggy's family," she admitted, pleased that there might be just a touch of healthy jealousy behind the question. "I was in tenth grade at the time. Rosy-eyed and romantic. Peggy and I dreamed of strolling the River Walk under the stars with the scent of tropical flowers all around us and adoring, drop-dead-gorgeous young men at our sides. Her brother Kevin heard us talking and teased us for the rest of the trip about it."

Joe half smiled. "I'd have liked to have seen you then," he said. "I bet you were a cute teenager."

"I wish you had been there," she answered, her tone openly flirtatious in an attempt to deepen his smile. "I can't think of anyone more perfect for fulfilling my romantic fantasies."

His eyes gleamed. "Maybe we could work on a few of those fantasies when we get home tonight," he suggested in a masculine purr. "I have a few of my own, as a matter of fact."

She swallowed hard against the sudden tightening of her throat. "I think that could be arranged," she said shakily.

Oh, how she loved hearing him refer to "home." She was beginning to believe that she wanted very much to make a home with—and for—Joe.

If only..., she thought again, and had to make a massive effort to keep her smile from fading.

The food was as good as Joe had promised, though Lauren wouldn't have cared if they'd dined on burgers and fries. The restaurant was quieter than the bar had been, the atmosphere enhanced with candles and flowers. They talked easily enough by being careful of their subjects, avoiding Joe's past and Lauren's current problems. Instead they shared their thoughts on politics and religion, books and movies, music and art. The sort of things, Lauren thought at one point, that two people would discuss during the early stages of a courtship.

Ridiculous analogy, of course, she assured herself hastily, and directed her thoughts quickly into less painful avenues.

Back in the car after dinner, Joe buckled his seat belt, waited for Lauren to do hers, then asked, "Do you like to dance? I know a nice lounge not too far from here."

Dancing? She made a deliberate effort to keep her jaw from dropping in surprise. "Do *you* like to dance?"

"I would with you," he answered quietly, sounding sincere enough to make her palms go damp.

She wiped them surreptitiously on her skirt. "I'd love to dance with you," she replied simply.

"Good," he said, and started the engine.

Any awkwardness either of them might have felt when Joe first took Lauren into his arms on the dance floor quickly vanished. The lounge was even darker than the restaurant had been, the lighting deliberately moody and intimate. The band was excellent, their volume high enough for enjoyment yet low enough for comfort. Their harmony was smooth and practiced, their musical selections an appealing mixture of oldies, soft rock and soft country. Whether intentionally or not, Joe had chosen a place that was ripe for romantic seduction.

Lauren was quite sure it had been intentional.

The top of her head came just to his jaw. Joe rested his cheek against her hair as they danced, fingers entwined, bodies close together. His breath ruffled the fine hairs at her forehead, and his light, late-evening bristle—he hadn't thought to shave before they'd left the cottage—tickled the soft skin at her temple when he brushed a kiss there.

She thought it entirely possible that she'd melt into an undignified puddle at his feet before the evening was over.

Whatever had been bothering Joe earlier seemed to have been pushed to the back of his mind. He was relaxed, attentive and charming, making her fall in love with him all over again.

It was an almost perfect evening, until she looked over his shoulder late in the evening and saw a man who looked ominously familiar watching her from a stool at the bar across the room.

She gasped and stiffened, stumbling to a halt in her dancing. Joe swiftly steadied her, then held her at arm's length to look at her face.

"Lauren?" Whatever he saw in her expression had obviously startled him. "What is it? What's wrong?"

Two couples danced by, passing between Lauren and the bar. When they moved away, she saw that the bar stool was now vacant, the man who'd been watching her gone. A cold chill slithered down her spine. Surely, she told herself anxiously, she'd been mistaken.

Joe's fingers tightened on her shoulders. "Lauren? *What's wrong?*"

Touched by the deep concern in his voice, she shook her head and raised an unsteady hand to rest on his chest. "Nothing. Sorry."

"Why did you stop dancing? You looked as though you'd seen a ghost."

Aware that they were drawing curious looks from the couples around them as they stood in the center of the crowded dance floor, Lauren took a step back. "Why don't we go back to our table. I could use a break—and a drink."

He led her through the crowd of dancers with more efficiency than courtesy. When they reached their table, he signaled for a waitress, then asked again, "What happened?"

Feeling foolish now, she squirmed in her undersized chair and answered reluctantly, "It's probably foolish. I'm sure I was mistaken."

"Mistaken about *what?*" he demanded, increasingly impatient.

"I thought I saw one of the men who tried to kidnap me sitting at the bar watching us dance."

Joe went still, so suddenly he could have been turned to stone. His voice was very quiet, unnervingly lethal when he asked, "Where is he?"

She quickly shook her head. "He's gone now. Really, Joe, I'm sure I was wrong. How could it be one of them? Who could possibly know we're even in Texas, much less in a dance lounge in Houston? It's not as if we gave anyone our itinerary for tonight. *We* didn't even know we were coming here until an hour and a half ago."

"Did you get a good look at him?"

"No. There were people between us and...well, I really wasn't paying that much attention," she admitted, remembering that she'd been much more interested in the feel of Joe's arms around her than in watching the other patrons of the lounge. "I just happened to meet his eyes across the room and—" she paused to moisten her lips before continuing "—for a moment, I had the feeling I'd seen him someplace before. And then I thought of the bigger of the two men who tried to grab me in Arkansas. That's when I gasped.

"I guess I hadn't realized how much it's still on my mind," she added. "I thought I'd put it behind me, but apparently I haven't. Not entirely, anyway."

"How could you, when it's still not even safe for you to go home?" Joe pointed out logically.

Lauren wished he hadn't phrased it quite that way. Rather than intimate and romantic, the bar now seemed dark and sinister. Beneath the tiny table, she slipped her hand into Joe's. "Would it be okay if we leave now? I'm getting a little tired."

He rose promptly, shaking his head at the waitress who'd finally headed their way in response to his signal of a few moments earlier. "Let's go."

Her attentive escort had become her vigilant body-guard again. Joe kept one hand at the small of her back as he hustled her through the parking lot to the car, his narrowed gaze constantly on the move. He checked the inside of the car before helping her in, then wasted no time sliding into the driver's seat, starting the engine and leaving the lounge behind as he headed toward Galveston.

"We're leaving tomorrow," he said abruptly, after nearly half an hour of taut silence.

Her eyes widened. She turned to stare at him. "Leaving? You mean, leaving Galveston?"

"Yeah. You can pack what you want to take with you. I don't want your father shipping your things anywhere. This time only my superior and your father will know where we are—and I wouldn't even tell your father if he weren't paying my fee. But I want it made clear to him that he's to tell no one where you are—and I mean just that. Not his secretary, no aides or assistants, no friends or relatives. No one."

Lauren was stunned. "You're doing this because I thought for a few seconds in a crowded bar that I saw one of the men who attacked me? Joe, that's crazy. You're overreacting. It was probably just some innocent by-stander who happened to resemble the guy."

"Probably," Joe agreed, seeming to believe her. "But we're still moving. I was going to tell you later tonight."

She frowned. "How long have you known?"

"Since I talked to my boss this afternoon."

"Where are we going?"

"Colorado. This time we're going to *my* place, and only two people other than us will know. I can keep you safe there."

Her palms had gone damp again, this time from fear rather than arousal. She twisted them in her lap. "What did your boss tell you that made you think we have to leave tomorrow?''

He answered with audible reluctance. "The guys who tried to grab you are in Texas. They were pulled over for a traffic violation in Beaumont, but they got away before they could be detained after the cop recognized their names from the APB out on them.''

"How close is Beaumont to Galveston?''

Joe's answer was grim. "Too damned close.''

Her hands tightened until the circulation to her fingers all but stopped. "Why didn't you tell me earlier?''

"I didn't want you to worry.''

That annoyed her enough to at least partially override the fear. "You didn't think I had the right to know?''

"I said I was going to tell you later,'' he reminded her. "I just wanted you to enjoy yourself for a few hours first.''

She sighed. How could she fault him for wanting her to have a few pleasant hours before the perturbing revelation he knew was coming? "You should have told me immediately,'' she felt compelled to say, anyway, though she knew there was no real censure in her voice.

Joe nodded. "Maybe,'' he said, obviously not convinced that he'd been wrong to wait. "But now you know.''

"So it could have been him,'' she whispered, thinking back to the man in the bar, straining to remember his features. "Even though it's crazy, even with almost nothing to gain, they may still be after me.''

"Probably not,'' he reassured her, reaching across the console to take her icy hand in his big, warm one. "But it never hurts to be careful.''

She twined her fingers with his, clinging desperately to the one source of security she found in a world that had once seemed so orderly and predictable but had suddenly become so uncertain and frightening.

She'd often felt frustrated and powerless in her life. But she'd rarely felt this vulnerable. She wondered if she was really as strong as she'd always believed Marcus Caldwell's daughter to be.

At the moment, she wasn't feeling strong at all.

Chapter Ten

Joe made sure nothing had been disturbed while they'd been away from the beach cottage. Everything was just as he'd left it, alarms set, other, more sophisticated security measures functional. The cottage was well protected, though not as well as the cabin in Colorado he'd be taking her to the next day.

After resetting the system, he turned to Lauren, finding her standing quietly behind him. Much too quietly. The laughter and animation that had lit her eyes during their impulsive outing had faded, leaving her pale and worried. He didn't like it.

He lifted his hands to cup her face between his palms, causing her to look up at him in surprise. She was so small, he mused, his thumbs stroking the delicate line of her jaw. So fragile, in so many ways. And yet so strong in so many others.

He'd never known another woman like her. He'd never admired anyone more. He'd never wanted anyone more. And he wondered if he'd ever be able to walk away from her.

Her arms slid around his neck as she suddenly pressed closer to him, obviously seeking reassurance. He wrapped his arms around her and hugged her almost tightly enough to endanger her rib cage. "You're safe with me, Lauren," he promised her recklessly. "No one's going to hurt you while I'm around. I swear."

"I know," she murmured, her face buried in his throat, her lips moving against his skin. "Just hold me for a minute, okay?"

"I'll hold you all night," he answered roughly, cupping her firm buttocks to pull her more tightly against him. "I'm going to make you forget everyone and everything but me. I'll make you feel so good you'll forget you were ever afraid of anything."

"Yes," she said, sliding one hand into his hair to bring his mouth down to hers. "Make me feel good, Joe. Love me."

Love me. An uncomfortable quiver went through him at the husky whisper, but he ignored it as he crushed her mouth beneath his own.

She was his, he thought with a sudden surge of protectiveness so fierce he shuddered with it. For tonight, she was his. And he'd kill anyone who tried to touch her.

Swinging her off her feet and high into his arms, he turned and strode toward his bedroom, needing to show her—and perhaps himself—just how thoroughly she belonged to him tonight.

She probably thought he was asleep when she whispered the words. They'd been lying in silence for a long time, their ragged breathing gradually slowing, their sated bodies limply entangled. The room was dark, silent, the sounds of the waves and the nighttime muted and distant.

His eyes closed, Joe had been savoring the feel of her, warm and bare against him, her hand resting over his heart, her hair tickling the underside of his chin, his mind filled with fresh memories of the most incredible love-making he'd ever experienced.

And then the silence was broken by a quiet murmur. Three simple words, said without ceremony, without expectation of response, yet they rocked him all the way to his toes.

"I love you," she whispered, and pressed a fleeting kiss to his throat.

Joe lay awake, staring wide-eyed at the ceiling, long after Lauren's soft, even breathing told him that she'd finally fallen asleep.

Lauren thought she'd seen all Joe's moods. She didn't even claim to interpret them, but she thought she knew them all. She found out during the early hours of the next morning that she still had a very long way to go before she'd ever fully know or understand this man.

Distant tenderness, she thought at one point, having tried for a couple of hours to come up with a term to describe his behavior since he'd awakened her for breakfast. He was considerate, thoughtful, even affectionate, touching her shoulder when he passed her, gently brushing a strand of hair away from her face before he kissed her good morning. And yet there was a new distance in his eyes—a guarded, almost wary caution that she simply didn't understand. She didn't know what had happened during the night—what she'd done or said—that would make him so skittish this morning.

There had been that one unguarded moment, of course...but he'd been asleep for a long time then. She just knew he had. So it couldn't be that, thank goodness.

Then, what? Worry about her safety? About the extent of her involvement with him? About her expectations from him? The latter was one she could reassure him about, should he ask. She expected nothing from him beyond the weeks or days remaining until she'd be free to return home. It would break her heart when it happened, but she was fully prepared for Joe to ride off into the sunset like the old television cowboy heroes he'd claimed to admire. She was ready for the eventuality, if not resigned to it. But she had no intention of telling him so unless he asked. That was one subject she just wasn't eager to discuss with him.

So, instead, she assumed a breezy, casual, deceptively cheerful demeanor, teasing him about overcooking the bacon that morning—"It's nice to know you don't achieve perfection *every* time you prepare a meal. I was beginning to feel intimidated!"—offering to help him pack for the move to Colorado, asking for his suggestions as to what she should take. He responded pleasantly enough each time, even teasing her in return, though Lauren knew his behavior was as forced as her own.

Joe took care of all the arrangements for their travel. Lauren didn't even try to speak to her father, though she listened openly to Joe's conversation with him. She could tell Marcus wasn't pleased that Joe had taken over without bothering to consult him first. She could only imagine her father's sputtering reaction when Joe started barking orders without leaving time for rebuttal.

"I don't want *anyone* told where we'll be, is that clear, Caldwell? And I mean anyone. Not your secretary, no assistants or aides or long-time family retainers. No friends or family. No one.... Okay, so you get the point. I just wanted to make it clear.... No, you don't need the number where we'll be. We'll contact you regularly. If you have any messages to send in the meantime, contact my boss. He'll notify me to call you... Hell, no, I don't think I'm going overboard! Those bastards have tracked Lauren down twice, Caldwell. If they find her again, it won't be from my carelessness and it had damned well better not be because of yours!''

Lauren bit her lip against a smile, picturing her father's reaction to Joe's curt tone. Few people had the nerve to talk to Marcus Caldwell that way. She was one of them. Joe, obviously, was another. She liked that.

But then, there were few things about Joe that she didn't like, she mused, her attention drifting from his part of the conversation. If only he weren't quite so secretive about his past, or his feelings. If only he weren't so firmly opposed to commitment. If only...

"Lauren?"

Her name, spoken in a tone that suggested he'd been trying to get her attention while she'd been lost in her own thoughts, made her blink and turn back to Joe. He'd hung up the phone, she noted. How long ago? "Yes?"

"Anything wrong?"

"No, of course not," she lied. "Is my father still speaking to you? He didn't fire you over the phone, did he?"

Joe's crooked grin flashed briefly across his face. "He wanted to, but his concern for you finally won out over his displeasure with me. That man really hates it when someone else takes charge, doesn't he?"

"Violently."

"Well, he's just going to have to get used to it for now. I've had enough of foul-ups that have haunted this assignment. From now on, we're doing things my way.''

Lauren's smile had vanished at his use of the word "assignment." Hadn't she become more to him than a job by now? Or was this his way of reminding her—reminding both of them, perhaps—that their relationship was only a temporary one? "I'm sure you know what you're doing," she said rather tonelessly.

He eyed her closely for a moment, but apparently decided not to question her sudden change of mood. "Better get your things together. It's time to go."

She nodded and turned toward her bedroom without speaking again.

They loaded the car in near silence, taking only the two small bags Joe had allotted each of them. He'd assured her that if she needed anything else, they could pick it up in Colorado. They needed to travel light for now, he'd said, and Lauren hadn't argued. She was getting accustomed to leaving everything behind and starting over. At least this time she'd have her toothbrush and a change of underclothes.

Her hand on the door handle, Lauren hesitated before opening it, looking wistfully at the beach where she and Joe had first made love. It was harder to leave this place than she'd expected, she realized. Oddly enough, she'd been happy here, despite the circumstances.

"Lauren?" Joe prodded impatiently, his own door already open, one foot already in the car.

She blinked away an inconvenient film of tears and climbed into the car, closing the door firmly behind her.

It made her feel a little better when Joe didn't immediately drive away after starting the car. He sat for a long, silent moment looking out at the beach. Reliving the same memories she had?

He didn't glance at her when he finally threw the car into reverse and pulled out of the parking stall beneath the cottage. Neither of them looked back as they drove away.

Joe would have felt comfortable betting everything he owned that no one followed them from the airport in Denver to his cabin in the mountains. The trip there took just over an hour. He'd taken every precaution he'd learned during the past eight years to make sure they got there in one piece. Lauren's safety depended on his expertise, which made this the most important assignment he'd ever handled.

Except for the season, the cabin looked exactly as it had last time he'd seen it a couple of months before. It had been winter then, the surrounding woods bare and gray, the ground blanketed with snow. Now it was springtime in the Rockies and the woods were fresh and green, the ground lush with grasses and wildflowers.

"It's lovely," Lauren said when they drove up to the cabin.

Joe tried to see the place through her eyes. The house was constructed of split logs, with a cedar shake roof, two rock fireplaces, and a deep, covered porch that ran the full length of the front of the house. It was built into the side of a hill, so that the front door was ground level, but the back door on a second story above the basement. A redwood deck crossed the back of the house, with a long flight of stairs leading down to the naturally landscaped backyard and into the dense woods behind. He'd designed the three-bedroom, two-bath house himself, and had done most of the construction.

He'd never really understood his compulsion to own a house, to have a place to call his own to return to on those rare occasions when he wasn't on assignment. During the long months of Ryan's recuperation after that fiasco in the Caribbean, Joe had been glad he'd built this place. It had been the perfect convalescence location. Joe and Ryan had both needed the solitude and the months of recovery from the trauma of what had almost happened.

He'd never really thought of it as a home. More as a refuge, a place where he could safely rest and regroup between jobs, a vacation retreat, of sorts. He'd never planned on bringing a woman here, or settling here permanently, or even adopting that cat he'd always meant to get some-day. After all, who'd watch it while he was gone? One of the main attractions of this place was its isolation. But he had the strangest reaction when Lauren complimented the cabin. He was almost as proud as if it *had* been "home." Maybe, he thought reluctantly, this place had come to mean more to him than he'd realized.

Emotional ties. He'd avoided them for so long—since he was five, to be exact. People, places, even houses—he'd tried not to get attached. As Lauren turned to smile her approval of the mountain sanctuary where he'd brought her, he understood that he hadn't been quite as successful as he'd hoped at avoiding attachments. The way Lauren's smile made his throat tighten was a perfect illustration.

"Not exactly luxury accommodations—it's not deco-rated as fancy as the place in Galveston—but we'll be safe here," he said nonchalantly, swinging bags out of the trunk of the car he'd rented at the airport in Denver.

She reached for her bags over his protests, insisting on carrying hers while he took care of his own. Joe was pleased to note that she'd made this trip much more easily than the one from Arkansas to Texas. She looked a bit tired, but still alert. Her sprained arm seemed to have healed completely and the bruises were gone from her face, leaving only the thin, fading scar from the cut on her forehead. She looked beautiful. Joe doubted that anyone seeing her for the first time would ever suspect she'd recently been through hell.

"I'll unlock the door," he said more gruffly than he'd intended, quickly turning away from the appealing sight of her.

He was all too aware that the cabin's decor was minimal, to say the least. A deep leather couch, two matching recliners, a sturdy coffee table and a TV were the only furnishings in the long, high-ceilinged living room. Nothing hung on the polished log walls, no rugs softened the tongue-and-groove wood floor. There were no knick-knacks or photographs on the split log mantel of the huge rock fireplace. The kitchen was neat, functional, made light and airy by a large window over the sink and the glass-walled bay window in which sat a round oak table and four bow-back chairs. The kitchen walls, too, were bare, and there were no plants or fancy canisters or even curtains to indicate the personality of the house's owner.

Leaving the bags in the living room as they took their abbreviated tour, Joe led Lauren into the closest bedroom. Again, he studied the room through her perspective. An oversize cannonball bed, triple dresser and single nightstand were the only furnishings. A handmade quilt he'd found in a local craft store served as a bedspread, and bare blinds covered the windows. The lamp on the nightstand was definitely of the discount-store variety, a plain blue ginger-jar style with a pleated white shade.

"I warned you it wasn't fancy," he reminded her, wondering if she would have rather stayed in the professionally decorated vacation home in Galveston.

"I love it," she answered with apparent sincerity. "Oh, I'd probably add a few decorations," she added when he looked at her in surprise. "Pictures and curtains, that sort of thing. But it's a beautiful home. You must be very proud of it."

He cleared his throat. "You can sleep here. This is my bedroom. I'll take the one down the hall. The one Ryan usually claims when he visits."

"I'm not going to turn you out of your own bedroom!"

Joe shook his head. "Ryan's stuff is all over the other room. It would be better if *I* bunk in there."

"I thought you said there were three bedrooms."

"The third doesn't have any furniture in it."

"Oh." She chewed her lower lip a moment, then gave him a look that let him know what she was going to say even before she spoke. "Is there really any reason for us to use different bedrooms? Couldn't you just stay in here...with me?"

Oh, yeah, there was definitely a reason for them to use different bedrooms. Many more nights of sleeping with Lauren in his arms and Joe didn't know if he could ever again sleep soundly alone. Since that had never been a problem for him before, he wasn't eager to experience it now. It was going to be hard enough to say goodbye to Lauren. He'd be a fool to let this go any further.

He shoved his hands into his pockets and studied the toes of his boots. "The other bedroom will be fine for me. I'll go get your bags now."

She didn't try to detain him, nor did Joe glance at her as he turned and left the room. Somehow he knew even without looking that her hurt at his less-than-subtle rejection would be mirrored in her expressive green eyes. And he wasn't at all sure how he'd react—what foolish things he might say—if he saw her pain.

* * *

By late evening, Joe's mood, which Lauren had earlier termed "distant tenderness," had deteriorated into what could only be called surly. His face had all the inviting warmth of a thundercloud, his tone was clipped, his few words spoken abruptly. He paced the cabin like a caged animal, his long, booted strides eating up the distance across the large living room without notably burning off his almost visible tension.

"We could take a moonlight walk in the woods," Lauren suggested, looking up from her knitting.

"No."

She lowered her needles to her lap and mentally counted to ten before speaking again, trying to keep her tone light. "Maybe some TV? A video, perhaps? I noticed you have quite a few titles on your shelves."

"Go ahead and watch one if you want." He didn't sound enthused.

"D'you have any board games?"

"No."

"What *do* you want to do?"

"Nothing."

"Fine." Annoyed, she folded her knitting and tucked it into its bag. "I think I'll turn in. I'm a little tired from the trip."

"Good idea. See you in the morning." His tone was brusque, his expression as detached as though she were a stranger who just happened to be sharing his accommodations.

She wanted very badly to hit him.

Instead she turned and walked from the room with every ounce of dignity she'd ever acquired from too many years of hiding behind her pride when it seemed she had nothing else to depend on.

Just as she stepped into her borrowed bedroom, she heard what sounded like a muffled curse and a crash from the living room. A crash that sounded suspiciously like an angry fist slammed against an unyielding wood wall.

"I hope he smashed his knuckles," she muttered, closing the door and wiping at a trickle of tears that infuriated her almost as much as Joe had.

She wished she had something convenient to blame for her inability to sleep. An uncomfortable bed, an intrusive noise, physical discomfort. Anything. But Joe's big bed was quite comfortable, though sadly lonely, the night was still and quiet, though hauntingly empty, and the only pain she was experiencing was centered somewhere in the vicinity of her bruised heart. There was only one reason she couldn't sleep—Joe. She missed him, as much as she tried not to.

How was it possible for her to still love and want him this much after he'd hurt her so badly?

He came into the room so quietly she didn't even hear him until she looked up to find him standing beside the bed, wearing only his jeans again. "I'm sorry," he said before she could ask why he was there. His voice was low, gruff, all the more affecting because he'd spoken so very quietly.

"You've been acting like a jerk," she told him, unwilling to let him off quite that easily.

He stood very still, holding her eyes with his own, his face just visible in the near darkness. "I know."

"You hurt me," she said, and this time there was more anguish than accusation behind the words.

His hands clenched at his sides, though he didn't move toward her. "I was trying to keep you from being hurt."

She dashed at her wet eyes with jerky, defiant movements. "You did a lousy job of it."

"Yes."

"Why?" she whispered, growing exasperated by his refusal to elaborate.

He hesitated, then made a vague, ineffectual gesture with one hand. "I don't want you to get hurt from this, Lauren. I can't make you any promises."

"I never asked for any promises," she reminded him curtly.

"I know. But—"

"But you know it isn't a casual affair for me," she finished for him, proudly lifting her chin. "That it has never been casual for me."

He flinched, though he masked the reaction almost instantly. "I know you don't do this sort of thing often."

"I don't do 'this sort of thing' at *all*," she corrected. "When I make love with someone, it's because I care. It has nothing to do with proximity or hormones or adrenaline or any of the other excuses you're probably about to offer. I care about you, Joe."

He made a choked sound that could have been a groan, or a swallowed protest. And then he shook his head. "Don't say that."

"Why? It's true."

"You don't even know me."

"You really believe that?"

He couldn't hold her eyes. He looked down at his bare feet. "This isn't really an uncommon situation," he said, doggedly logical. "I saved your life, and now you feel dependent on me for your safety. It's only natural that you—"

The vulgar word with which she interrupted him seemed to startle him, despite the perfectly calm, even slightly amused tone in which she said it. "I haven't naively romanticized you, Joe. I'm not a fawning girl, awed by the manly hero who is bravely taking care of her. I don't think you're particularly noble and you're a long way from being perfect. You're arrogant and abrupt and autocratic—just like my father, in some ways, which annoys me a great deal. You've been on your own for so long that you've become rather selfish, and you're so accustomed to having your own way that you tend to sulk when you encounter resistance. And you don't have to try very hard at all to be a real bastard—again, like my father."

Joe's frown carved deeply into his shadowed face. "You can say all that and still claim to care?" he asked, sounding rather like a sullen boy whose pride had just been effectively bruised.

Her smile was tremulous. "Yes. Because you can also be very sweet and thoughtful and considerate and gentle. Because you've held me when I was afraid and nursed me when I was wounded and ill and made me smile when I wasn't sure there was anything left to smile about. And because I know why you think you have to hide your vulnerabilities behind that stone-hearted loner facade you've constructed."

"You think so?" If he'd tried to sound amused or bored, he'd failed. He sounded reluctantly intrigued.

Sitting up in the bed and letting the covers fall to her waist to reveal the thin nightgown that was all she wore, Lauren shrugged. A spaghetti strap fell from her shoulder with the movement, and she noted in satisfaction that Joe's attention was instantly drawn there, proving he wasn't quite as detached as he seemed to feel compelled to pretend.

"Yes, I do know you," she told him flatly. "You learned how painful it could be to lose the people you love—your parents, your brothers and sisters—maybe others at some point, I don't know. But you decided it was easier—safer—to stay aloof, to hide yourself away in this mountain cabin and not let anyone get too close.

"You're close to your partner—so close that you were badly shaken when he was injured—so close that you're worried sick about him now, even though you don't want to be. But you haven't let anyone else mean that much to you. I think the reason you've been so cold today is because you realized you were becoming more involved with me than you meant to," she added daringly. "And I think that scares the pants off you."

"It's not *my* feelings I'm worried about," he retorted roughly. "I've never expected anything more than a temporary affair—pleasant, but completely over when this is all behind us and you're free to return home."

"That's all I've ever expected, as well," she returned. She didn't say it was all she'd ever hoped for. That, of course, would be a lie. One he wouldn't believe, anyway.

She noted he hadn't argued about her amateur analysis of his reasons for not getting involved. He probably realized that was one argument he couldn't win. Both of them knew his fears dated back to his traumatic childhood. Joe thought those unpleasant experiences had scarred him for life. Lauren believed passionately that the right woman's love could help him heal the scars.

Maybe she just wasn't the right woman, she thought wistfully. Or maybe, damn it, she was—and he just wasn't giving her the chance to prove it.

Seeing the open skepticism on his face, she rose to her knees and stared fiercely into his eyes. "Why did you come in here tonight, Joe?"

He glanced swiftly down at the very thin fabric covering her breasts, then seemed to force his gaze back up to her face. "I wanted to apologize. For being so curt with you earlier."

"In the middle of the night? You could have waited until morning."

"I couldn't sleep. I thought you might be awake, too."

"I was, obviously. But not because I was lying in here nursing my wounded sensibilities."

His eyes narrowed, his frown deepening in response to her husky tone. "What do you mean?"

"I was lying in here missing you," she told him, lifting one hand to run a fingertip down the center of his sleek, bare chest. "Remembering the nights we've spent together. Remembering the first time we made love—on the beach, in the moonlight. So excited and impatient we didn't even take time to remove all our clothing."

Again, he made an odd, choked sound deep in his throat. "Lauren—"

"And in the shower. Remember how you washed all of me? How careful you were not to miss a spot?"

"Lauren, don't—"

"And I thought of how no one else has ever made me feel the way you do—and I wondered if anyone else ever would."

"I can't—"

She swayed forward and wrapped her arms around his neck. "I want you, Joe. I want you so badly. Can't we forget about what might happen tomorrow? Can't we just savor whatever time we have together now?"

She felt the tremor that went through him even as his hands rose slowly to her waist, his palms warm through the thin silk of her nightgown. "I don't want to hurt you, honey," he murmured again, his voice raw.

"Maybe it's already too late for that," she admitted, then held him more tightly when he stiffened. "I don't care," she said. "I want you. Tonight. Now."

"But—"

"Joe," she whispered against his lips, his throbbing arousal pressing into her stomach giving her encouragement. "Don't you want me?"

"*Want you?*" He spoke harshly, incredulously. His hands tightened at her waist, drawing her even more closely against his tautly held body. "God, Lauren, I want you so much it's eating me alive."

"Then make love with me. Please."

Her husky whisper accomplished even more than she'd expected. Joe gave a low, fierce growl and tumbled with her to the bed, his mouth closing over hers with a savage passion that elicited an answering wildness from her. Her fingers dug deeply into his shoulders, and her legs locked tightly around his lean hips, holding him prisoner even as he laid claim to her pliant curves.

He wasn't promising her tomorrow, she thought with her last vestige of sanity. But he hadn't been able to stay away tonight.

For now, she'd have to be content with that.

Chapter Eleven

Lauren had just stepped out of the shower and belted her robe when Joe tapped on the bathroom door the next morning. "Come in."

When he opened the door, she noted that he was frowning, but without the intensity of the day before. He'd woken in a better mood this morning, his eyes still grave, though not as wary as they'd been yesterday. He'd made love to her with a hunger that hadn't been abated by the passion they'd shared during the night. Lauren wondered if she'd finally convinced him that she wasn't nursing hopes for promises he wasn't willing to offer, that she was willing to accept whatever he wanted to give for now without thought of the future.

"We don't have any coffee," he said, bringing her abruptly out of her sensual memories. "I forgot to get any."

"No coffee?" she repeated in only slightly exaggerated dismay. "Not even instant?"

"Not even that."

"This could be a very ugly morning," she warned him gravely.

His mouth twitched in faint amusement at her announcement. "I know. I feel the same way about it."

"Isn't there a store anywhere close by?"

"Closest one's about ten miles away."

"That's not so bad." She waved a hand to indicate that he was fully dressed. "What are you waiting for?"

He looked thoughtful. "I don't like leaving you alone."

"How long can it take for you to go ten miles to pick up coffee?"

"Thirty minutes, round trip."

"I think I can survive that long. More than thirty minutes and you'll have a raving, hysterical caffeine addict on your hands."

He chuckled and leaned over to kiss her. "Surely it's not that bad."

"Trust me. I have friends who won't even attempt to speak to me before I've had my coffee."

Joe's smile faded. "Male friends?"

"*All* my friends," she corrected, inexplicably cheered by that small sign of jealousy. "Go get coffee, Joe. I'll be fine."

"You're sure?"

She pointed toward the door, her manner imperious. "Go."

"I'm gone. Don't unlock the doors. Or—"

"Would you go, already?"

He laughed softly and kissed her again before leaving. Lauren was still smiling when she turned back to the mirror to brush out her wet hair.

She was just fastening the snap on her jeans when she heard the noise coming from the direction of the kitchen. A clanging sound, as though someone was going through cabinets. She froze, then looked at her watch. Only fifteen minutes had passed since Joe had left. He couldn't possibly have made a twenty-mile round trip and bought coffee in that short a time. Had he changed his mind or was someone else . . . ?

The sound came again, louder this time, followed by a muffled curse. A man's curse.

Lauren pressed a hand to her heart, which she could feel pounding even through her plaid cotton blouse. Joe wouldn't have changed his mind without telling her, she reasoned, chewing her lower lip. He would have known she'd think she was alone, and hearing noises would startle her. Joe thought about things like that.

So who was in the kitchen? And how had he gotten past the security system? *And what was she supposed to do now?*

She thought of the gun Joe kept in the nightstand. Had he taken it with him?

Tiptoeing with exaggerated stealth, she crossed the room and slid open the drawer, holding her breath for fear that it would squeak or otherwise give her away. It opened silently, revealing the heavy weapon inside.

Her hand clenched into a fist. She couldn't do this, she thought in sudden panic. She couldn't use the gun, even if she had to. She didn't even know how!

But then a muted crash came from the kitchen, and she snatched the gun out of the drawer, its weight suddenly comforting in her shaking hand. Maybe she couldn't actually fire it, but perhaps she could use it to detain her uninvited guest until Joe returned, she reasoned. He'd be back in only a few minutes.

Unless something happened to delay him . . . like an ambush waiting outside for him.

She swallowed a groan at the melodramatic turn her thoughts had taken. But was the possibility really so slight? Wouldn't it be logical for anyone wanting to get to her to try to eliminate Joe from the scene first? Every thriller movie she'd ever seen suddenly flashed through her mind—and all of them involved great danger to the endangered heroine's protector. She had to make sure Joe was safe.

Taking a firmer grip on the weapon, she made her way quietly across the bedroom and slipped out the open doorway into the hall. Her eyes trained on the kitchen door, the gun held in front of her—she tried not to notice the way it shook in her hands—she forced herself forward. She really didn't want to do this, she thought desperately, but she couldn't let Joe walk unsuspectingly into potential danger.

Remembering scenes from television police shows, she raised the gun in front of her, gripped in both hands, barrel pointed toward the ceiling. She pressed her back to the wall beside the kitchen door, listening to the sounds coming from inside. Why was the intruder apparently going through the cupboards? What was he looking for? A weapon? In the kitchen?

Maybe, she thought in a sudden rush of hope, the intruder wasn't dangerous at all. Maybe it was just a mischievous teenager, or a homeless person, looking for food. In which case, the sight of the gun in her hands would probably send whoever it was bolting for safety, which would suit Lauren just fine.

She drew a deep breath, said a quick, silent prayer, and kicked the kitchen door open, the gun leveled in front of her. "Freeze!" she shouted, feeling rather foolish even as the word left her mouth.

He stood at the counter, paralyzed in surprise, one hand stuck in a cabinet, the other dangling in midair at his side. "What the—?"

Lauren almost dropped the gun at the sight of his achingly familiar features. "*Joe!* Damn it, you scared me half to death!"

"Er—"

Her own paralysis vanishing, she pelted across the room and landed in his arms, trembling in delayed reaction. "Don't ever, *ever* do that to me again! Don't you realize that I could have shot you?"

His arms went automatically around her, as though to steady her. "The thought crossed my—"

She pulled his mouth down to hers before he could finish the sentence, smothering the words with her lips. Just the thought of what could have happened had things gone wrong made her knees go weak. She clung to him, trying to express her apology in her kiss.

And then she went still again. Though he returned the kiss cooperatively enough, something just wasn't right.

She drew back an inch to look at him, finding him smiling quizzically down at her, a look of startled question in his pale blue eyes.

His face was the same as always, but the smile was different, an infectious, wholehearted grin she'd never seen rather than the rare, crooked smiles she'd treasured before. His brows were lifted, and she noted the scar that bisected the left one and ran several inches across his temple. Not a new wound, but a scar that had faded to a thin white line, hardly noticeable.

But not something she would have missed before this.

She gasped and jerked herself out of his arms, the gun waving wildly at her side. "You're . . . you're not—"

"I'm not Joe," he finished for her, keeping a wary eye on the gun. "I'm Ryan. His brother. And you are—?"

"My God," she whispered, utterly astounded. *"Twins."*

"Yes." He reached out and nimbly removed the weapon from her slack fingers. "Why don't I hang on to this for a while? Just a precaution, of course."

Twins! And Joe hadn't even told her his partner Ryan was also his brother.

It hurt more than she would have expected. Her heart ached and her shoulders slumped a bit as she realized that this was just one more sign that Joe was still holding her at a distance, still refusing to let her become a part of his life. She'd been such a fool to even hope she'd been making progress with him.

"Um, not that I'm complaining about that warm welcome or anything, but maybe you'd like to introduce yourself?" Ryan suggested, watching Lauren with a searching intensity that belied his lazy drawl.

Even his voice was different now that she'd stopped to notice, she realized, drawing herself back together. "I'm sorry. I'm Lauren. Lauren Caldwell."

"A, er, friend of Joe's, I take it."

"He's my . . ." She paused, bit her lip, then shrugged. "He's my bodyguard."

Ryan's scarred brow lifted again, but he only nodded. "I see."

Lauren pushed a still unsteady hand through her drying hair and shook off the remains of her sudden depression. "I'm sorry," she said again. "It's just that you startled me so badly I've forgotten my manners."

"Then I'm the one who should be apologizing," Ryan assured her. "I didn't know Joe was staying here. He's never come here while on an assignment. To be precise, he's never brought *anyone* else here that I know of."

She didn't allow herself to be pleased. After all, this time Joe had really had nowhere else to take her. "The circumstances are a little unusual," she admitted. She waved toward the table in the bay window. "Would you like to sit down and talk until he gets back? I'd offer coffee, but we're out. Joe's gone after more."

"Coffee. That's what I was looking for when you, um, apprehended me." His eyes danced with inner amusement at the memory.

Lauren groaned, knowing how foolish she must have looked doing her imitation of a TV cop. But already she was beginning to like Joe's brother, finding herself taken by his calm humor and soothing charm. She took a chair at the table, Ryan sinking into the one at her right. "Joe's been very worried about you," she told him. "Apparently, he expected to hear from you several days ago."

Ryan looked regretful. "I know. I got delayed by some complications with the assignment I was working on. I was going to get in touch with him as soon as I'd had a cup of coffee."

"Twins," she said again, still finding it hard to believe. It was difficult not to stare at this man who looked so very much like the man she loved—and yet so oddly different.

"He didn't tell you." It wasn't a question.

"He didn't even tell me you were his brother. He called you his partner."

"I am—when he works with a partner."

She frowned, remembering when Joe had told her about his siblings. She still remembered their names. "Jared, Layla, Miles, Shelley and Lindsay," she murmured. "And Bobby. He didn't mention a Ryan."

Ryan had gone very still. "Joe told you those names?"

She nodded, eyeing his stunned expression. "Of course."

He shook his head, slowly. "No 'of course' to it. Joe never talks about the past, never mentions our siblings to *anyone*. Are you and he, uh . . . ?"

"We're involved," she answered carefully, "but not seriously. At least not permanently. He's told me very little about his past. To be honest, I don't even know his—*your*—last name."

Ryan ran a hand along his jaw, looking thoughtful. "Interesting," he murmured. Lauren couldn't help noticing that he didn't offer to supply the name, either.

"Which brother are you?"

He blinked, as if trying to understand the question, then nodded in comprehension. "Bobby. But I haven't used that name since I was nine. Never did care for it. Joe started refusing to answer to 'Joey' at about that same time."

She couldn't help smiling. "That doesn't surprise me."

Ryan's expression changed mercurially, from speculative to flirtatious. "So, tell me, pretty lady, what is my brother guarding that delectable body of yours from, hmm?"

"From obnoxious Lotharios with tired, worn-out lines," Joe answered crossly before Lauren could think of anything to say. "Belt up, Ry."

Lauren looked around to find Joe standing in the kitchen doorway, a brown paper bag in the crook of his left arm, his attention focused on his brother. Though he wore his usual scowl, Lauren noted the gleam of relief in his eyes. He was extremely pleased to see Ryan, despite his gruff manner. Did he really feel it necessary to hide his feelings, even from his own brother?

"Just tell me there's coffee in that bag you're holding and you can call me all the names you want," Ryan said fervently.

Joe set the bag on a counter, though he didn't immediately empty it. Instead he kept his attention focused on his brother. "Where the hell have you been?"

"The wilds of Utah. Sorry I didn't call, but the communications facilities were somewhat primitive, to say the least."

"Utah?"

"Yeah. Turned out that's where Kelsey had the Blaine jewels stashed. I staked out his place there for over two weeks—under conditions I don't even want to think about, much less discuss—but I got him. Cold."

"Way to go, Ry." Lauren wondered if the hint of pride in Joe's voice was as obvious to Ryan as it was to her.

"Thanks. The insurance company was rather pleased with me."

"For the recovery of nearly a million dollars' worth of jewels? I should think they were."

"You were working as an insurance investigator?" Lauren asked, intrigued by the conversation, which seemed awfully casual considering how worried Joe had been about Ryan during the past few days. The twins appeared to have a rapport that let them communicate without superfluous words or outward demonstrations of their feelings. Despite his blasé demeanor, Joe was obviously relieved to see Ryan, just as Ryan must have known how concerned his brother had been. A close—but rather eccentric—relationship, apparently.

Ryan answered her question. "Insurance companies tend to be our most steady customers. Insurance fraud is big business these days."

"It sounds like fascinating work. But doesn't it get dangerous?"

Joe and Ryan gave identical, perfectly synchronized shrugs. "Sometimes," Joe conceded.

"We're careful," Ryan added. "Joe, are you going to make that coffee or am I going to have to do it myself?"

Joe gave him a look that should have made him quail, but Ryan only grinned, obviously accustomed to his brother's ferocious posturing. Lauren watched them both in fascination, thoroughly intrigued by this new insight into Joe's personal life.

Joe glanced at her before turning to the coffee maker, then spoke over his shoulder as he started the coffee. "I take it you two have met?"

"We sort of introduced ourselves," Ryan answered, tongue in cheek.

Lauren squirmed in her seat as she remembered the way she'd kissed him.

Joe looked swiftly from her flaming cheeks to Ryan's rather smug smile.

"By the way, Joe. I think this is yours." Ryan pulled Joe's handgun out of the waistband of his jeans and laid it on the table.

"What are you doing with my gun?"

"Lauren was, um, showing it to me, weren't you, sweetheart?"

She cleared her throat. "Is that coffee ready yet? I'm about to go into serious withdrawal here."

Joe looked at her for another long moment before turning back to the coffee maker. She let out a long, silent breath of relief that he didn't immediately pursue the subject of the gun, though she didn't for a moment believe the matter was closed for good. Ryan gave her a cocky wink when she happened to meet his eyes across the table, just as Joe turned back to slide her coffee in front of her. She took it gratefully, almost scalding her mouth with her first greedy sip.

He poured the next cup for Ryan. Lauren watched as he lightly touched his brother's shoulder when he handed him the cup. "Good to see you, Ry," he said quietly.

Ryan cuffed Joe's arm with a loosely clenched fist. "You, too, Joe. Thanks for the coffee."

That was all. Joe poured himself some coffee, divided the cheese Danish he'd picked up while he was out, and sat down to have his breakfast with them, sentiment apparently behind him. But that one brief moment of communion between the brothers had brought a misty film of tears to Lauren's eyes, which she hid by concentrating fiercely on the Danish in front of her until she was sure she had her rather shaky emotions fully back under control.

Ryan exchanged only a few words with Joe before turning back to Lauren. She could tell he was trying to think of a tactful way to find out about her without prying. Taking pity on him, she answered the question he hadn't yet asked. "There are some people trying to kidnap me," she explained. "They're members of a hate group based in Chicago that calls itself the Chosen Ones. Their leader, a man named Cal Bullock, is being tried for several crimes, including aggravated assault and attempted murder, and my father is the prosecuting attorney. They seem to think that holding me will have some influence over the outcome of the trial. My father hired Joe to keep me safe until the trial ends, which should be within the next few weeks."

"The Chosen Ones," Ryan repeated thoughtfully. "I've heard of them."

Joe nodded. "Sleazy bunch. They nearly killed Lauren trying to grab her in Arkansas a couple of weeks ago. We moved to a safe house in Galveston, but had to relocate here when the two guys who tried to grab her were spotted in Beaumont, Texas, apparently on their way to us."

Ryan's frown deepened, making him look so much more like Joe that Lauren couldn't help staring again. She found it fascinating to be confronted by this identical image of the man she'd grown to love. Yet some deep part of her was aware of the many differences between them, despite appearances. "How'd they find out where you were?" Ryan asked Joe.

"Obviously a leak somewhere, since it happened twice."

"Has it been plugged?"

"Not that I know of. Counting you, only three people know where we are now. Miller, of course, and Lauren's father."

"Who's Miller?" Lauren asked.

"Our boss." Joe turned back to Ryan after the concise reply. "Will you be around for a while?"

"As far as I know."

"Good. I didn't like having to leave Lauren alone this morning. Even with the precautions we've taken, I'm not going to feel comfortable until Bullock's convicted and the other two are apprehended."

Lauren wondered if Joe was relieved that they were no longer alone for more than the reason he'd just given. Did he plan to use Ryan as a shield between them, a way of holding her at a distance during the remainder of this "assignment"? He'd made it clear enough that they'd been getting too close for his comfort. With Ryan around all the time, the intimacy that had first brought them together would be dispelled.

Not that it would matter to her, of course. Even had Ryan been around from the beginning, Lauren believed she would still have fallen as hard and as fast for Joe. There was just something about him that drew her, something she hadn't been able to resist no matter how hard she'd tried. And she had tried.

Realizing she'd drifted into her own thoughts while Joe and Ryan continued to discuss her case, she brought her attention back to the conversation just in time to hear Joe ask, "So you haven't spoken to Miller since you wrapped up the assignment in Utah?"

"As a matter of fact, I have. I called him at three this morning. Got him out of bed," Ryan added with obvious relish.

Joe grinned, noting the characteristic spark of mischief in his brother's eyes. "I'm sure you enjoyed that."

"Immensely."

Joe would have loved to have heard the beginning of *that* conversation. "He didn't have anything else for you to do now?"

"Well, he did have one suggestion of what I could do with myself. I chose to decline that particular request." And then Ryan's smile faded. He glanced at Lauren, then back at Joe. "There was one other thing Miller and I discussed that I need to talk to you about later. Something he's been monitoring in regard to us. It's a, uh, personal matter."

Joe frowned, realizing Ryan was being obscure because Lauren was listening. Apparently reaching the same conclusion, Lauren picked up her empty breakfast plate and coffee cup and started to rise. "I think I'll go do my nails or something. I'm sure the two of you have a lot to talk about."

She was smiling, obviously understanding there were matters the brothers would need to discuss in private. But something in her eyes made Joe reach out without even thinking about it. He put a hand on her wrist to hold her in her seat. No matter how often or how intimately they'd touched before, the feel of her soft skin beneath his hand shook him. The faint tremor beneath his fingers told her that she, too, was affected by the contact.

What the hell was happening between them? he asked himself in uneasy exasperation. Why couldn't he even touch her without feeling as though he'd been kicked in the chest? And why couldn't he send her out of the room now, even knowing she had no business sitting in on a private discussion between himself and Ryan?

"The three of us are going to be sharing close quarters for at least the next few days. We can't send Lauren out of the room every time we talk. She can be trusted to keep anything she hears confidential."

He wondered if he'd made a mistake when he saw the soft light appear in her expressive green eyes. Had he encouraged her to indulge in fantasies that just couldn't come true?

He'd tried so hard not to make promises, not to lead her on. He had nothing to offer her, no real home to give her, no safe future to share with her. He was a man accustomed to living in the shadows, risking his life for the rush of adventure and a promise of pay. He had no business getting involved with a woman like Lauren—a woman obviously destined for a home and a family and a comfortable life in suburbia. All the things he simply didn't know how to offer her.

But he still couldn't send her away.

He pulled his gaze away from Lauren's and turned back to Ryan. And found himself getting uncomfortable all over again. Ryan was watching him with a speculative interest Joe couldn't misinterpret, obviously fascinated by Joe's behavior with Lauren. Joe understood, of course. He'd never behaved like this, never felt like this with any other woman. He didn't even try to delude himself that Ryan wouldn't recognize the symptoms. His twin knew him all too well.

"What situation has Miller been monitoring?" he asked gruffly, self-consciously aware of the two sets of eyes trained so intently on him. "And what does it have to do with us?"

"Let me pour another cup of coffee and I'll give you a summary of what Miller told me," Ryan replied, reaching for his cup.

Lauren beat him to it. "I'll get it," she said. "I wanted another cup, myself. Joe?"

"Yeah, thanks." He kept his eyes on Ryan. "Well?"

Ryan smiled a thank-you at Lauren when she handed him his fresh coffee. Joe noted that she returned it brightly. She'd never smiled at him that way, he found himself thinking. She seemed completely at ease with Ryan in a way she'd never quite been with him. He wasn't quite sure how to interpret her behavior, or his own reactions to it. "Ryan?" he prodded, aware that his voice had grown curt.

Ryan sighed. "He's never learned the art of patience," he murmured to Lauren. And then, when Joe growled a warning, he started to speak, rather hastily. "There's a P.I. in Dallas named Tony D'Alessandro. He's been looking for us, and coming damned close to tracking us down. Miller found out weeks ago, but he wanted to look into it before mentioning it to either of us. He's been throwing the guy off, pulling the usual dodges. But this D'Alessandro seems to be the persistent type."

Ryan had Joe's full attention now. "Why the hell is a P.I. in Dallas looking for us?"

Ryan took a deep breath before answering. "According to Miller, the guy's representing our brothers and sisters.

They've all been reunited during the past year. Now they're trying to find us."

Joe set his coffee cup down so fast the hot beverage splashed over the side and onto his hand. "Damn," he said, hardly aware of the sting.

Ryan's announcement was the last news he'd expected. And probably the least welcome, as far as Joe was concerned.

Chapter Twelve

"I've talked to Miller every day since I started this assignment," Joe complained, breaking the taut silence that had followed Ryan's announcement. "Why the hell didn't he mention this to me?"

"Maybe I caught him off guard by getting him out of bed with my call," Ryan suggested.

"Miller's never off guard."

"That's true. Well, maybe he didn't want to interfere with your concentration while you're watching out for Lauren."

Joe started to retort that nothing ever interfered with his concentration during an assignment. He swallowed the words before they left his mouth, all too aware that Lauren had blown that perfect record of his all to hell. Instead he asked, "What did Miller tell you?"

"Only that he'd gotten word through his security contacts that our records were being searched. He followed the usual procedures in tracking down the source of the investigation, and they led him to this P.I. D'Alessandro's first contact was with an organization that reunites separated families. Layla had apparently registered several years ago.''

''Was she the one who hired the P.I.?''

Ryan shook his head. ''Miller doesn't think so, though his information is somewhat sketchy. D'Alessandro's client confidentiality seems to be pretty tight.''

Joe's brows lifted. ''It must be if even Miller couldn't find out all the details.'' Miller was quite simply the best in the business. Obviously the P.I. Joe's siblings had hired was damned good, as well.

Though she'd been listening avidly, Lauren hadn't spoken until now. ''They've all been reunited?'' she asked with interest. ''All five of the others?''

Ryan was still looking at Joe. ''Four,'' he said quietly. ''That's all of them now.''

Joe steeled himself for the rest, trying to keep the conversation brusque and impersonal. ''Who didn't make it?'' he asked, reading Ryan's expression.

''Miles. Died in a car accident several years ago. Miller found out when he was verifying D'Alessandro's investigation to make sure it had nothing to do with any of our old cases.''

A hazy image of an eight-year-old boy wavered in Joe's mind despite his efforts to push it away. Miles. Mischievous blue eyes, a splattering of freckles, an infectious grin. Always the comic, rarely serious. The only time Joe remembered seeing Miles cry had been the day they'd been separated. And now he was dead.

Lauren had been watching him for the reaction he knew he'd kept from his expression. Or had she come to know him better than he'd wanted her to? Her green eyes were liquid with compassion when she touched his rigid hand and murmured, "I'm sorry."

He shook her off. "I hardly even remember him," he lied flatly. He turned back to Ryan. "How's our cover?"

"Solid. Miller assured me we won't ever be found unless we choose to be. Not even this D'Alessandro guy is that good."

"Good."

Lauren was trying very hard not to be hurt by Joe's rejection of her sympathy. She knew he was shaken by Ryan's announcement, knew it wasn't easy for him to be faced with his past, especially when he seemed to be having problems dealing with his present. But his blunt approval of the security of his cover made her open her eyes wide and blurt out, "You aren't even going to contact them?"

He flicked her a glance that told her to back off. "I'm not planning on it."

Lauren looked at Ryan, wondering if he felt as strongly about it as Joe. She found him watching his brother with a thoughtful expression that made her wonder if he agreed with Joe, at all. Did Ryan *want* to be reunited with his siblings? And if he did, would he stand up to his twin?

Apparently not. "You want me to tell Miller to handle it as he sees fit?" he asked Joe.

Joe nodded. "Or I'll tell him myself, next time I check in. He'll know how to put an end to this without it getting messy. As far as D'Alessandro will ever know, you and I are as out of his reach as Miles."

"All right."

Lauren couldn't believe what she was hearing. "That's it? You aren't even curious about them?"

Joe's frown deepened. "You and I have talked about this, Lauren. It's best this way."

"Best for whom?" she demanded, her exasperation with him shattering her usual tactfulness. "For your brothers and sisters, who have no idea if you're dead or alive? For you? For Ryan?"

"Look, I'm glad they've found each other again, okay?" Joe snapped. "It's good that they're not alone now. But Ryan and I haven't *been* alone. We've been together all along—and that suits us fine. We don't need a bunch of strangers expecting us to become part of their family. We haven't made mistakes like that since we ran away from our last foster home when we were sixteen."

"Sounds to me like you're doing an awful lot of talking on Ryan's behalf," Lauren retorted. "You haven't even asked him if he wants to see his family again."

Joe flicked Ryan a glance. Ryan reached out to pat Lauren's hand, his expression kind, as though he appreciated her concern even as he gently rejected it. "Joe *is* my family," he told her. "The only family I've had—or needed—since we were five years old. He's right. We don't even know these other people."

"And you have absolutely no interest in seeing your brothers and sisters again. No curiosity about what they've become or whether they're well or happy," Lauren said skeptically.

"Not really," he answered, but he didn't quite meet her eyes when he spoke. Watching him closely, she realized that his expression was more open than Joe's, more readable in some ways, even to her. She hadn't missed the way he'd hesitated before he answered. She knew Joe hadn't misread the signs, either.

"Ryan?" Joe's eyes, too, were trained on Ryan's face. "We are in agreement about this, aren't we?"

"That it would be easier to forget Miller ever mentioned this? Oh, yeah, we agree on that."

"But you can't help wondering, can you, Ryan? You can't help thinking you'd like to see them again, even if just one time," Lauren said daringly, braving Joe's anger because this seemed so desperately important to her. She had the feeling that if she didn't say anything now, the subject would never be brought up again. That Joe and Ryan, however they privately felt about it, would put the whole incident behind them, their one opportunity to be reunited with their family forever lost.

Obviously, this was none of Lauren's business. But she couldn't bear to let it end like that. Joe should have sent her out of the room when he'd had the chance, she thought stubbornly.

He looked as though he agreed with the unspoken sentiment. "If Ryan wanted to see them, he'd tell me. Wouldn't you, Ry?"

Ryan cleared his throat. "Well, uh..."

"Damn it, Ryan, are you going to answer me or not?"

Ryan sighed and shook his head. "Damn it, Joe, I don't know *how* to answer you!" He ran one hand through his hair in the gesture Lauren had seen Joe use so often. "I agree with you that it would probably be better to forget all about this. To go on the way we have been, with no strings or commitments or burdensome expectations. But... well, part of me can't help wondering what they're like now. Is Jared still the dependable, quiet type? Is Layla happy? Do we have nieces and nephews? Do any of them look like us now? I'm curious, Joe, but I'm not certain I want to get involved in this."

Joe's mouth twisted into a semblance of a grin. "I guess I should have expected you to be curious," he admitted. "You're always curious."

Ryan smiled. "Despite your many dire warnings about the fate of that damned cat."

"And how many times have I had to say I told you so when your curiosity got us into trouble?"

Clearing his throat again, Ryan shrugged. "A few, I guess."

Joe's snort was more expressive than words could have been. After a moment he sighed and said, "You give this some thought before we talk to Miller. *Serious* thought. If you really want to see them, I'm certainly not going to interfere."

"But you won't go with me if I choose to do so?"

Joe grimaced. "I doubt it. If you go, you can assure them that I'm fine, that I look just like you, if they're interested, and that I've made a good life for myself. That's all they need to know."

"I haven't really decided to go," Ryan reminded him. "It could get sticky. Uncomfortable."

"You can almost bet it will. But it's your decision."

Ryan nodded. "I'll think about it."

Lauren's chair squealed loudly against the wooden floor when she shoved it back from the table. "If you'll excuse me, I think I'll go freshen up. I'll be in my—in the bedroom if anyone needs me."

Joe suppressed a wince when the kitchen door swung closed behind her with considerably more force than necessary. He wasn't eager to meet his brother's eyes, but knew it was inevitable. "Well?" he said, almost in challenge.

Ryan was trying hard not to grin, without visible success. "I think Lauren's miffed with you," he murmured.

"She's royally ticked off," Joe corrected, knowing "miffed" was far too mild a description. "For some reason, I just seem to have that effect on women."

"You know, I've noticed that."

"And mentioned it a few times." Joe decided it would be prudent to change the subject. "So how'd you find the Blaine jewels? Where'd Kelsey have them stashed?"

"My case wasn't nearly as interesting as yours," Ryan replied, refusing to cooperate. "Tell me about Lauren."

Joe shrugged, his gaze trained on the dregs of his coffee. "What's to tell? She's a CPA from Chicago who's gotten unfairly mixed up in one of her father's cases, to her regret. Her father's a real jerk, by the way. Seems to think he's infallible, even though his orders have endangered Lauren more than once during the past couple of weeks."

"I didn't ask about her father, I asked about Lauren."

"What do you want to know?"

"Is she single?"

"Yes."

"Available?"

Joe scowled. "What's that supposed to mean?"

"Joe, the woman is gorgeous. Interesting, too. You can't blame me for wanting to get to know her better. I was just trying to find out if you and she . . . I wouldn't want to intrude on your territory, of course."

"Lauren isn't *anyone's* territory," Joe snapped, his hand tightening around the handle of his coffee cup. Was Ryan serious, or teasing him? Sometimes it was hard even for Joe to tell.

"So you're not sleeping with her or anything? It's okay for me to make a move on her?"

The handle snapped cleanly off the fragile mug. Joe stared at it for a moment, realized Ryan was doing the same thing, and tossed the broken handle down with a growl. "Damn it, Ry."

Both hands held palm outward in a gesture of surrender, Ryan said quickly, "Sorry. I was only kidding. I didn't realize this was serious."

"It's *not* serious. Not the way you mean, anyway," Joe grumbled.

Propping both elbows on the table, Ryan rested his chin on his fists and watched his brother across the table. "I've never seen you like this about any woman. Never known you to talk about our past to the few women you've dated. Never seen you look at one the way you were looking at Lauren when she left the room. Don't tell me it's not serious, Joe. I know you too well."

Exhaling wearily, Joe lifted one shoulder in a half-hearted shrug. "It ends when the assignment ends. That's all it can be."

"I don't think Lauren's in full agreement with that. I saw the way she was looking at *you*, too."

"Give me a break, Ry. You really think I'm going to settle down in suburbia with a pretty accountant who makes no secret that she wants marriage and kids and extended family and all the trappings that go with that life?"

"I think it might be the best thing that ever happened to you," Ryan said with unexpected gravity.

Joe's scowl deepened. "Yeah, right. Obviously you've forgotten what happened to you two years ago."

"I've forgotten a lot of what happened to me two years ago," Ryan agreed evenly. "But I fail to see what that disaster has to do with you and Lauren."

Joe deeply regretted his reckless accusation. He knew it still bothered Ryan a great deal that he'd lost all memory of the four weeks of his life prior to his attempted murder during a dangerous assignment. Retrograde amnesia, the doctors had called it, a result of the massive trauma Ryan had sustained. No one knew exactly what had happened to Ryan during those weeks. And Ryan had admitted that he'd spent many sleepless nights plagued by questions, wondering. It particularly bothered him that he didn't remember the woman, that no one knew who she'd been, how she'd been involved in the attack on Ryan, if at all. "I'm sorry, Ry. I wasn't thinking."

With the innate understanding that had always marked their relationship, Ryan waved off the apology. "Okay, we know I apparently got involved with a woman during a case and it ended badly."

"It ended with you too damned close to dead."

"Right. But that still doesn't have anything to do with you and Lauren."

"It shows you can't put any stock in a relationship begun under these circumstances. Everything's too precarious, too unsettling. Lauren's scared and confused and looking for some semblance of security in a world that has suddenly gone crazy and dangerous, and I've been there for her. When this is over, when she goes back to her own life, she'll realize I don't fit in. I don't belong there." It was the first time Joe had put the possibility into words, though the thoughts had haunted him for days.

"You think she's feeling dependent on you because you're guarding her life? That she's mistaking that dependence for something more permanent?"

Joe nodded. "Right. If she'd met me under normal circumstances, at a party in Chicago or whatever, she probably would have seen right off that I didn't fit in to her life. That nothing could come of an involvement between us."

"And your feelings for her? Proximity? Temporary physical satisfaction?"

Joe shoved his chair back and surged to his feet, tossing the broken coffee mug into a wastebasket. "It's more than that, okay?" he snapped, offended for Lauren's sake, even though he knew Ryan hadn't meant the words. "Lauren's no cheap tumble. But I'll get over it. I always have before."

"Maybe because it was never real before. Maybe this time it is."

"Then I'll learn to live with it. It's best that way."

"You seem to be saying that a lot today. Who are you trying to convince, Joe? Me—or yourself?"

Joe's shoulders stiffened. "Drop it, Ryan."

"Right. But if you need to talk—"

"I know."

Neither of them needed to say more.

When Joe came into the bedroom, Lauren was sitting on the bed, her back propped against a pile of pillows at the headboard, trying to concentrate on a book. She'd been staring at the same page for at least ten minutes without reading a word. Joe closed the door behind him, his expression slightly wary as he looked at her.

"You, uh, still mad?" he asked, moving to sit beside her on the edge of the bed.

"Not mad," she said with a sigh. "Exasperated."

"I know you don't really understand me—"

She gave a short, humorless laugh. "No kidding."

Joe reached out to brush a hair from her cheek, his touch so gentle it made her throat tighten. "I don't mean to seem hard or unfeeling," he said, holding her gaze with his own. "I just do what I have to do to get by. Can you understand that?"

"I'm trying," she whispered, afraid that all her feelings were mirrored in her eyes for him to see. Unable to hide them. "I'm trying so hard to understand you."

He stroked his thumb over her lower lip, slowly, tenderly. "Maybe it would be better if you stopped trying."

"I can't do that," she murmured, her lips moving against his thumb.

He was staring at her mouth now, apparently fascinated by the shape of it. She felt her lips tremble. "You're going to be hurt, Lauren," he said in a voice ragged with regret.

"Yes." She didn't even try to argue with him.

"I didn't want that to happen."

"I know."

"If it helps, I care about you, Lauren. It isn't casual. And it isn't just sex. But—"

"But..." she echoed with a slight sigh, not needing to hear the rest. It touched her deeply that Joe had admitted he cared about her. She knew it hadn't been easy for him, that he hadn't said the words just because he knew she wanted to hear them, but because he meant them. Yet they both knew he'd still be walking away when the assignment was over.

"You must wish you'd never laid eyes on me."

"No," she whispered, tossing the book aside to throw her arms around his neck. "Whatever happens, I'll always be grateful I had this time with you, Joe."

He pulled her close with a low groan that vibrated against her breasts. "God, Lauren, you're so—"

Whatever word he might have used was lost when she pressed her lips to his. His arms tightened around her, his tongue stabbing into her mouth with a turbulent hunger he made no effort to conceal. Lauren told herself that whenever she thought of him in the future, whenever she lay awake during long, lonely nights thinking of him, missing him, she'd always remember that he really had wanted her. That he hadn't been able to resist the attraction between them any more than she had. That he'd truly cared—if only for a little while.

Long, heated minutes later, Joe pulled his mouth from hers with a gasp. Resting his forehead against hers, he breathed deeply, obviously trying to bring himself under control. Lauren closed her eyes and savored his nearness, reveled in the feel of his hard, strong arms locked so securely around her.

Finally he lifted his head. His smile was a bit strained, but genuine. "You could put a man in the hospital, Lauren Caldwell. After last night, and this morning, you'd think I'd be too tired to want you again this soon, but I do."

She smiled wickedly and ran a leisurely hand down his chest to his stomach, enjoying the way his muscles rippled beneath her palm in instinctive response. "So what's stopping you?"

"My brother's waiting in the next room," he said ruefully, catching her hand just before it wandered into dangerous territory. "And I'm supposed to check in with Miller and your father this morning. This will have to wait."

She pulled her hand from beneath his to give him one intimate, promising squeeze. "Remember where we left off."

He groaned, caught her wrist again, and pulled her hand firmly away. "I doubt that I'll be able to forget."

She pulled back as reluctantly as he did, sternly ordering her quivering nerves to settle down. Climbing off the bed, she picked up a hairbrush and repaired the damage Joe's hands had done during their kisses. "You and Ryan are very different, aren't you?" she asked, keeping her eyes on her reflection in the mirror.

"In some ways," Joe agreed, moving to look out the window until she was ready. "Apart from the physical, of course."

"I was talking about the differences in your personalities, of course," Lauren said musingly. "I noticed almost immediately that Ryan wasn't much like you. Even when I was kissing him—"

"When you were *what?*" Joe roared, spinning back to face her.

"I thought he was you!" she retorted, dropping the hairbrush on the dresser. "I was so relieved to see you—er, him—after he'd scared me half to death making noises in the kitchen, that I just kissed him before I stopped to notice he wasn't you. Come on, Joe," she added when Joe didn't look entirely satisfied with the explanation, "the two of you look just alike, and you hadn't told me you had a twin. How was I supposed to know it wasn't you?"

"I guess he let you know soon enough."

Lauren couldn't help smiling as she thought of the way Ryan had politely cooperated with the kiss. He'd been a perfect gentleman, of course—almost.

Joe's frown deepened. "Lauren?"

"Well—"

"I'll strangle him."

She laughed. "He did try to tell me, Joe. It just took me a minute to start listening. Nothing happened."

He grunted and turned back to the window.

Lauren picked up a tube of lipstick, lightly painting her smile. "It really is amazing how much you look alike. I take it you're identical, and not fraternal twins?"

"Yeah. Carbon copies."

"That's fascinating. I remember studying identical twins in science and psychology classes in college. I always thought it would be incredible to have that sort of bond with someone. Do you and Ryan have any psychic experiences, like knowing when the other is in pain or anything like that? I've read some amazing stories about that sort of thing."

"I knew when Ryan was hurt two years ago." Joe's eyes were haunted with old memories when he turned back to look at her. "Even before anyone called me, I knew something was horribly wrong with him. I called Miller while they were still trying to locate me."

"That must have been awful for you."

"Miller told me during that call that Ryan wasn't expected to survive the night," Joe answered bleakly.

"Oh, God." Lauren couldn't even imagine how Joe must have felt to hear that. Already, she recognized the strength of the bond between the brothers—a bond formed by their birth, strengthened by years of having no one else to care about. What would have happened to Joe if Ryan hadn't survived? she wondered. How would he have handled a loss that devastating?

"I almost broke my neck getting to him," Joe murmured, apparently lost in his own thoughts. "You wouldn't believe what he looked like when I got there. Tubes and monitors taped to almost every inch of him, half the bones in his body broken."

"His face must not have been damaged. Other than that small scar on his forehead, he still looks just like you."

"His face was okay, but he did receive a head injury that left him in a coma for several days. After he regained consciousness, he hardly remembered his own name. Took months for him to get all his memory back. Now he remembers everything but the four weeks or so prior to the injuries. The doctors have said he'll probably never get those weeks back."

"Are there any other remaining problems?"

"Nothing too serious. Occasional back trouble. Infrequent migraine headaches. Nothing bad enough to keep him from working, obviously."

"How long did it take him to recover?"

"Almost a year."

"And you nursed him during that time," Lauren said, thinking of the way he'd so competently taken care of her after pulling her out of that stream.

"I took care of him, along with a team of rehab techs. He and I lived here until he was ready to go back to work. He drew disability pay, of course, and I had enough savings stashed away that I didn't need to work for a while."

Every time Joe showed her a glimpse of his past, Lauren felt as though she understood so much more about his behavior with her. He must have been terrified at the thought of losing Ryan. And that would only have reinforced his fear of getting too close to anyone else. After losing his family so young and going through a series of unsuccessful foster home placements, he'd grown wary of *any* attachments, no matter how fleeting. Which was one of the reasons he had fought so hard against becoming involved with her.

Joe shifted his feet, glancing toward the door. "I'd better make those calls. Your father'll have the national guard down on us if I don't check in soon."

She nodded. "Go ahead. I think I'll get a cold drink and go out on the back deck for a while. I need some fresh air. Tell Dad I'll talk to him later, okay?" Her day had been eventful enough without another painful, stilted conversation with her father.

"Sure you don't want to talk to him?"

"Not now. But if he insists, I'll be out on the deck."

Joe's face took on that hard set she recognized as utter determination. "If you don't want to talk to him now, you don't have to talk to him. I'll take care of it."

She'd just bet he would. Joe was the first man she'd ever known who struck her as being fully capable of handling Marcus Caldwell. Maybe that was one of the things she admired most about him, she thought, watching him stride from the room with his broad shoulders braced and his head held high. One of the many things she found admirable about this complex, lonely man.

Chapter Thirteen

Lauren was leaning against the deck railing, watching two squirrels chase each other through the thick branches of a nearby tree when the glass door opened behind her. Glancing over her shoulder, she smiled. "Hello, Ryan."

"Wonder if you'd say that so easily if Joe and I were wearing the same clothes," he mused, closing the door behind him and moving to stand beside her at the railing.

"I think I would," she replied seriously, remembering her conversation with Joe. "Now that I've spent time with both of you, I think I'd know the difference right off, even if I couldn't see the little scar on your forehead."

Ryan touched that scar with a self-conscious gesture. "I keep telling Joe he needs to get one just like it. I've even offered to give him one on occasion."

Lauren smiled. "I'm sure you've wanted to." She knew the feeling well.

"My brother can be...difficult, at times," Ryan agreed.

"I've noticed," Lauren assured him dryly.

"But you care about him, anyway, don't you?" Ryan asked perceptively. He smiled when she looked quickly up at him. "You can always tell me to butt out if you want to," he assured her. "I'm not very good at taking hints, but I can usually follow a direct order."

"I care about him," she said instead. It made it easier to know that Ryan, too, loved Joe, and understood him even better than Lauren did. "But I'm not nursing any false hopes. When this assignment is over, he's going to walk away. And there's nothing I can do to hold him, no matter how badly I want to."

Ryan sighed. "You're probably right," he said.

She tried not to be disappointed by the response. After all, he was only agreeing with what she'd already said. Maybe she'd secretly wanted him to offer some hope.

"It's not that he doesn't care," Ryan said quickly, obviously reading the pain in her eyes despite her efforts to hide it. "He does, Lauren. I've never seen him look like this with any other woman. And he's never gotten personally involved with an assignment—he's been a fanatic about that. So his feelings have to be pretty strong for him to overcome that deeply ingrained willpower of his."

"I know he cares," Lauren replied quietly, candidly. "It just isn't enough."

She seemed destined to love men who couldn't offer enough in return, she thought sadly. Her father. The one man she'd cared about before Joe. Joe, himself. Would she ever fall in love with a man who was willing to love her completely in return? Or was she fated to live alone, remembering what she'd had with Joe, mourning what they could have had if he'd only tried?

"Joe has his reasons for being the way he is, Lauren."

"I know most of them. And I understand. I just...wish things were different."

"So do I, sweetheart. For your sake, and for Joe's," Ryan said softly, reaching out to touch her cheek with a gentle finger. "You'd be good for him."

She blinked away a film of tears and attempted a smile. "You don't even know me."

"I don't have to. It's enough for me to see the way Joe looks at you."

She drew a deep, unsteady breath. "Thank you, Ryan. For being so kind. For caring."

"He's my brother," Ryan answered simply, his hand still at her cheek.

The door opened abruptly behind them. Joe stood in the doorway, glaring at them. Lauren and Ryan stepped quickly apart. Almost, Lauren thought in irritation, as though they'd been caught doing something they shouldn't have been. "What's going on out here?" Joe asked.

"I'm seducing your woman," Ryan returned, sounding as exasperated as Lauren felt. "And doing pretty well at it, I might add. Go away."

"For heaven's sake, Joe, we were only talking. What did you find out during your calls?" Lauren asked to change the subject. "Have there been any developments?"

"Come inside. We need to talk."

Lauren didn't like the worry she suddenly saw in his eyes. She felt her own widen. "What is it?" she demanded. "Is it my father? Has something happened to him?"

She'd been so confident that her father's security was practically impregnable that she really hadn't worried too much about his safety during the past two weeks. Had she been wrong? Had he...?

"Your father's fine, Lauren," Joe assured her.

Her knees went momentarily weak with relief. She clung to the railing to steady herself for a moment. Her relationship with her father might be strained, but she loved him. He was her only family. She didn't want to lose him. "Something's wrong," she said, seeing that Joe's expression was still grave. "What is it?"

"Come inside," he repeated. "You, too, Ryan."

Joe barely gave them time to be seated in the living room before he spoke again. "There was an attempt on your father's life this morning, Lauren. Someone took a shot at him as he entered his office. He wasn't hurt. He's fine," he repeated immediately when she opened her mouth in horror to speak.

"They're getting desperate," Ryan said.

Joe nodded. "The trial resumes in a few days, and they obviously know Caldwell's got a hell of a prosecution put together. It's stupid for them to think he's the only one with a guarantee of getting a conviction, but apparently they believe if he's out of the way, Bullock's got more of a chance of getting off."

"My father's the best," Lauren said simply. "Everyone knows that."

"Maybe." Joe didn't sound quite as convinced. "Anyway, his security has been doubled—and so has yours, by the way, Lauren. Ryan, Miller said to tell you you're on payroll as of this morning. We're both assigned to guard Lauren."

"That's the nicest assignment I've had in a very long time," Ryan said with a smile for Lauren. It touched her that he was obviously trying to make her smile in return, that he knew how distressed she'd been at hearing about her father's close call. Ryan was a very sweet man, she thought wistfully. So why was she so utterly certain that she could never love him the way she'd grown to love Joe?

Joe was watching her and Ryan with a brooding expression. "Why is it necessary to double my security?" she asked him. "I thought you said we were perfectly safe here."

"Joe and I have learned never to take anything for granted," Ryan answered instead. "Even the best plans aren't perfectly foolproof. Especially when you're dealing with a bunch of desperate lunatics like those so-called Chosen Ones."

"But only Miller and my father know where we are," Lauren argued. "How could anyone find us here? Unless we were followed, of course," she added nervously.

"We weren't followed," Joe said flatly.

"Sweetheart, if Joe says you weren't followed, you can bet your virtue on it," Ryan assured her. "And you can be equally confident that no one's going to find you through Miller. Your father, now..." He looked to Joe.

"Caldwell insisted on knowing the address where his daughter was being kept, but he swears he's told no one," Joe explained. "I tend to believe him, this time."

Lauren bit her lip as she thought of her father's one weakness—a compulsive need to write down everything, no matter how trivial or private. It was his way of making absolutely sure he never forgot anything. She thought of mentioning the habit to Joe, then decided to spare him that worry. After all, she reasoned, her father wouldn't recklessly endanger her safety. If he had written this address down, the information would be securely locked away with all his other ultraconfidential papers.

"Lauren?" Joe had been watching her more closely than she'd suspected. "What is it?"

"Nothing," she replied, deciding she was worrying needlessly about trivialities. She was safe here. She had Joe and Ryan to guard her. The bumbling oafs who'd tried to grab her in Arkansas wouldn't stand a chance against these two. "Really, it's nothing," she assured Joe. "I'm just concerned about my father."

"He'll be okay, Lauren," Ryan assured her.

She gave him a smile. "I'm sure you're right."

"Anyone getting hungry?" Ryan asked then, pushing himself to his feet with what Lauren was beginning to recognize as characteristic restlessness. "I'm hungry. How about lunch?"

"I'll fire up the grill and we'll have hamburgers," Joe said. "Okay with you, Lauren?"

"Yes, that sounds fine," she agreed absently, not really caring about menus. Still, Joe and Ryan were obviously trying to keep her from brooding about her father's safety, or her own. The least she could do would be to cooperate. She forced a smile. "I'll slice potatoes for French fries."

Joe and Ryan continued to exert themselves to entertain Lauren during the afternoon. With irrepressible, rarely serious Ryan around, even Joe loosened up some. Or was it because he felt more comfortable now that he and Lauren weren't alone? She couldn't help wondering even as she giggled at one of Ryan's jokes.

Ryan was a bit more willing to talk about their past than Joe had been. It was Ryan who told Lauren about the first time he and Joe had run away from a foster father who'd forcefully tried to curb Joe's stubbornness and Ryan's recklessness. They'd been nine years old, and they'd spent two cold, hungry weeks on the streets before they'd been found and taken to another home. "It was great," Ryan added. "We had a hell of a time."

Lauren lifted an eyebrow and looked at Joe, who seemed uncomfortable with Ryan's conversation but hadn't made any effort to stop the reminiscing. "It may not have been great," he said, "but it beat the hell out of most of the homes we were stuck in."

"Remember that one idiot social worker who said we'd be easier to handle if we were placed in separate homes?" Ryan asked, an old anger hardening his expression until he looked even more like his twin than ever.

Joe's voice was grim. "I remember."

"Separate homes? Identical twins? That's the most as-inine suggestion I've ever heard!" Lauren was furious on their behalf.

"It wasn't taken very seriously," Ryan admitted. "But that was the second time we ran away."

"And when you were sixteen, you ran away for the last time."

"Right." Ryan glanced at Joe in approval. "Joe's told you that, has he?"

"Mmm. How did you support yourselves?"

"Odd jobs. Running errands. Pumping gas. Cleaning stables. Painting barns. Sacking groceries."

"Whatever it took," Joe added.

"And then you connected with Miller?" Lauren asked, cocking her head in curiosity.

"Not Miller. His predecessor. Miller's not much older than us," Ryan explained. "Seven years ago, Joe walked into a security office in Denver and asked for a job. He'd gotten tired of manual labor, he said. Wanted something with a bit more adventure. Anderson—the guy before Miller—saw something in Joe he liked. Then when I came into the picture, he saw some potential in having twin op-eratives on occasion. Especially when he found out we didn't have any ties or commitments keeping us from tak-ing any particular assignments. He trained us, made us get our high school equivalency certificates, and put us to

work. And we've been at it ever since, sometimes as part-
ners, sometimes separately."

And often dangerously, Lauren added to herself. No
wonder Anderson had approved of their lack of family or
commitments. "When did Miller take over?" she asked.

"Couple of years ago. We weren't sure about him at
first, but he's okay," Ryan approved.

"Have you been thinking about going into another
business, too?" Lauren asked Ryan, thinking of Joe's
confession that he'd felt as though he'd been losing his
edge lately, particularly since he'd met her, she remembered uncomfortably.

Ryan looked at Joe so quickly that Lauren realized she'd
just let something slip that perhaps she shouldn't have.
"You thinking of quitting?"

Joe shrugged. "It's crossed my mind."

"You haven't mentioned it." Even Lauren heard the
trace of hurt in Ryan's voice. She wished she'd kept her
mouth shut.

"Because I haven't made any decisions. Hell, I wouldn't
know what else to do even if I quit," Joe said crossly.
"Believe me, Ry, if I ever make any life-altering decisions, you'll be the first to know."

Lauren twisted her fingers in her lap and kept her eyes
on the floor.

Joe pushed himself to his feet. "I'm going to have a slice
of that chocolate cake Lauren made yesterday. Anyone else
want any?"

Following the brothers into the kitchen, Lauren made a
vow to keep the conversation light and impersonal for the
remainder of the day. Joe was right. It was a lot safer that
way.

* * *

They decided to watch a movie after dinner that evening. Lauren had been rather surprised by the extent of the video and print libraries in the otherwise sparsely fitted cabin. Now she suspected that Joe had stocked up on the books and movies during Ryan's long convalescence.

After a friendly three-way debate about what to watch, they settled on *The Final Countdown,* an early 1980s time-travel movie involving a modern U.S. aircraft carrier mysteriously transported back to the days just prior to December 7, 1941. Lauren had never seen it, but she liked the cast—Kirk Douglas, James Farentino, Martin Sheen, Katharine Ross—and was intrigued by the premise. She particularly enjoyed hearing Joe and Ryan argue heatedly about what might have happened had the U.S. been prepared for the attack on Pearl Harbor and how the direction of the war, and the resulting shaping of world politics, would have been affected by the knowledge.

She realized that the twins couldn't possibly have received much in the way of formal educations during their turbulent youths, but both seemed intelligent and well-informed as they discussed history and politics. She thought of all the books she'd discovered here in the cabin, and of Joe's pleasure in reading during his spare time. The school of life, she mused. Possibly more valuable than her bachelor's degree, in the long run.

Everything she learned about Joe and Ryan made her admire them more. And she grew even more depressed at the thought of having them leave her life now that she'd met them, of never seeing them again. How could she bear to say goodbye?

"Lauren?" Joe sounded quizzical as he finally got her attention. "Didn't you like the movie?"

She glanced at the television screen and noticed the rolling credits. She vaguely remembered the ending, though she'd given it only half her attention. "It was very interesting, Joe."

"Not an Academy Award winner, but I like it," Ryan commented, pushing the Rewind button. "Katharine Ross just looks so damned good in those short shorts."

Lauren smiled.

"Anyone want anything else to eat or drink?" Joe offered.

Lauren groaned. "I've eaten enough during the past few days to last me for weeks. I'm getting a little tired. I think I'll turn in." She glanced at Joe from beneath her lashes as she spoke, wondering if he'd sleep with her tonight, or whether he'd continue to use his brother's presence as an excuse to start pulling back.

"You go on," Joe said, as though reading her mind. "I'll be in later."

She tried to keep the relief out of her voice when she answered as steadily as possible, "All right. Good night, Ryan."

He gave her a smile that would probably have weakened her knees had she not been so particularly vulnerable to Joe's rare, crooked grins. "'Night, sweetheart."

"Stop it, Ry," Joe muttered.

Ryan looked innocently offended. "Stop what?"

Lauren was still smiling when she closed the bedroom door behind her, though her smile faded as soon as she found herself alone.

True to his word, Joe slipped into the room a few minutes later. He caught her unprepared. She hadn't expected him quite that soon.

Wiping hastily at her eyes, she kept her back to him as she continued to stare out the window, as she had been before he'd walked in. "I thought you and Ryan would talk a while longer." She was pleased that her voice sounded steady enough. She'd been afraid it would betray her with a quaver.

"You shouldn't stand by the window at night like that."

"The lights are off," she pointed out. "No one can see me." Joe couldn't, either, now that he'd shut the door and closed them into near darkness. She was profoundly grateful for the shadows. She quickly wiped again at her damp cheek, determined to get her shaky emotions under control before turning to Joe.

"Come away from the window."

The curt order annoyed her, but she complied, making her way to the bed without turning on the bedside lamp. Aware that Joe was watching her much too intently through the shadows, she started to chatter. "The movie was interesting, but time-travel themes always drive me crazy. All those bizarre questions—like, could the guy who stayed back in the past have witnessed his own birth if he'd visited the hospital on that day? What if he'd accidentally run over his own father with a car before he—?"

"Lauren." He said her name quietly, but it was enough to make her go abruptly silent. He took a step closer to the bed. "Are you crying?"

"No!" she said, too quickly. "Of course not." It made her absolutely irate that her eyes filled again at the same time the words left her mouth. Thank heaven for the darkness, she thought.

Joe snapped on the light.

"You *are* crying," he said accusingly, his eyes narrowed on her damp eyes and probably reddened nose.

"I'm not crying," she insisted, snatching a tissue out of the box on the nightstand. "I'm just tired. Could we please go to sleep now?"

"Damn it, Lauren." He ran a hand through his hair, tousling it. His expression held a mixture of guilt, regret, and typical masculine bewilderment.

"Just come to bed, Joe," she said wearily, sinking into the pillows and pulling the covers to her chin. "It's getting late." Later than he knew, she thought, almost feeling their remaining minutes together ticking away.

He sat on the edge of the bed beside her, his hip pressing against her thigh through the thick quilt. "Are you frightened?"

"No." *Not the way you mean,* she thought sadly. *I'm only afraid of watching you walk away, of trying to live the rest of my life without you in it.*

"Are you crying about . . . well, about us?"

"Joe, please. Couldn't you just let it go tonight? I'm just tired and confused and maybe a little scared. Surely you can understand that."

"Yeah. I guess I can."

"Come to bed, Joe," she whispered again. *Hold me. Let me pretend you're mine for just a few more hours.*

He hesitated another moment, then turned out the light. Leaving his clothes in a pile on the floor, he slipped beneath the covers. And then he pulled her roughly into his arms, his hand on the back of her head as he cradled her against his shoulder. "This will all be over soon, Lauren. You'll have your life back—your career, your apartment, your friends."

Her memories. "I know."

"You'll be fine."

"Yes."

"Then there's nothing to worry about, is there?"

Pressing against his hand, she tilted her face up to his. "Joe?"

"Mmm?"

"Just shut up and kiss me, okay?"

He muttered something unintelligible and covered her mouth with his. Not interested in listening to any more of his forced reassurances tonight, Lauren wrapped her arms around his neck and slid her tongue into his mouth, effectively silencing him. Joe didn't seem inclined to put up any resistance.

He made love to her so thoroughly, so tenderly, so very sweetly, that there were tears on her cheeks again when she finally fell into an exhausted sleep. Even as she slid into unconsciousness, she heard her own voice murmuring, "I love you."

There was no reply.

She hadn't expected one.

Long after Lauren fell asleep, Joe lay awake, his arm around her, his eyes focused blindly on the ceiling. He had one of his perturbing feelings, an uneasy foreboding that he'd had on other occasions just before something bad happened. He wished he knew whether this feeling now was due to Lauren's precarious emotions—or something else.

Growing restless, he finally slid out of the bed, careful not to disturb Lauren, and pulled on his jeans. Maybe a glass of milk or something would help him relax, he thought, silently leaving the bedroom and heading for the kitchen. Ryan's door was closed, no light coming from beneath it. He was probably catching up on the rest he'd had to forgo during his recent assignment. He'd offered to stand guard during the night, but Joe hadn't thought it necessary. There was no reason to believe anyone knew where Lauren was, he'd pointed out, and the security alarms would go off if anyone tried to get in. They were safe.

He opened the refrigerator and pulled out the carton of milk, his thoughts still dwelling broodingly on the tears Lauren had tried so bravely to hide. The tears that had made him want to promise her anything she wanted even as they'd convinced him more surely that he had nothing of value to offer her.

Maybe he'd have reacted faster if he hadn't been so deeply absorbed in his thoughts of Lauren. Maybe he wouldn't have frozen for that one brief, critical moment out of fear for her when the shrieking alarms suddenly pierced the silence of the night.

A shotgun blast destroyed the lock in the outside door, followed by a powerful kick that sent the door flying back against its hinges. Joe whirled and reached to the back waistband of his jeans for a gun that wasn't there. He hissed a curse beneath his breath, turned, and threw himself toward the kitchen doorway, knowing Ryan would be on his way—and armed.

The bullet struck him in the back, slamming him forward into the cabinets. His head struck wood with a crack that exploded inside his skull, pitching him into darkness even as he fell. The last sound he heard was Lauren's scream.

I'm sorry, Lauren. Oh, God, honey, I'm so...

Chapter Fourteen

"I'm...sorry. Joe, I'm so sorry," Lauren sobbed, watching in horror as he fell, an ominous red stain spreading across his bare back. Because of her, she thought numbly. This was all because of her. She dropped to her knees and reached for him.

The tips of her fingers had just brushed his skin when a rough hand grabbed her arm and jerked her backward. It was the man who'd shot Joe; he gripped the still smoking handgun in one huge paw while clutching Lauren with his free hand. She recognized him as the big man who'd found her in Arkansas.

"Let's go," her captor yelled to his companion over the squawk of the security alarm. The alarm that hadn't proven as effective as Joe had confidently believed, Lauren thought dully, her burning eyes still focused on his ominously still body. If only he'd been in the bedroom, close to his weapon, given just a moment of warning. Why had he been in the kitchen? Why...?

A sharp jerk on her arm made her realize her captor was trying to drag her toward the gaping outside door. She fought him, determined to stay with Joe. "No!" she screamed, kicking, pulling, slapping at the hand that held her. He was trying to pull her to her feet. She used all her weight against him, refusing to cooperate, her bare feet tangling in the hem of her long cotton nightgown.

He hit her across the cheek with the butt of the gun clutched in his fist, making her gag at the all-too-familiar pain. This was a nightmare, she thought, her senses reeling drunkenly, her body sagging in momentary paralysis from the blow. It couldn't be happening again.

The sound of a gunshot crashed through the room, adding to the general noise and confusion. "Let her go!" Ryan yelled from the kitchen doorway. He was standing partially behind the doorjamb, a deadly looking gun in his exposed hand, its barrel trained on the man who held Lauren. "Now!"

He dodged behind the wall when the second man fired the shotgun from the outer door.

"Damn it, Jack! Would you be careful with that thing?" Lauren's captor roared, ducking and giving another jerk on Lauren's arm. She cried out at the pain, which felt as though he were pulling her shoulder right out of its socket.

Ryan fired again. There was a high-pitched squeal from the outer door, followed by a thud and a clatter.

"Jack!" the big man yelled, yanking Lauren off the floor and into the crook of one meaty arm despite her resistance. His back to the outer door, he held her against him, the handgun pressed to her temple. He took a step backward, dragging her with him, his eyes trained on the doorway behind which Ryan crouched. "Jack?" There was no answer from behind him.

"Let her go," Ryan yelled again.

"You stay back or she's dead. You got that?" An edge of panic had crept into the man's voice. Lauren's stomach tightened. If he panicked, if he lost what little control he had, there was no predicting what he might do.

The barrel of the gun was cold and hard against her skin.

He took another step backward, his boot brushing against Joe's bare, outstretched foot.

Joe came off the floor in an explosion of activity that caught all of them off guard. He made a wild grab for the gun even as Lauren threw all her weight to one side, knowing it was her one chance to help Joe and Ryan put an end to this. Her captor stumbled, squeezed off a wild shot, then bellowed in rage when Ryan threw himself into the melee. Ryan's fist slammed full strength into the bigger man's jaw. The meaty hand fell away from Lauren's arm as he crumpled to the floor.

The bigger they are...

The frivolous, incongruous phrase flashed through Lauren's mind before she was fully aware that it was over, that she was safe.

Keeping his weapon trained on the downed assailants, Ryan opened a cabinet and flipped a hidden switch. The alarm stopped abruptly, leaving a hollow silence in the kitchen.

Lauren turned to Joe, who stood in the center of the room, swaying on his feet, his torso soaked with blood. His skin was starkly pale beneath the purpling bruise on his forehead. He met her eyes with what appeared to be a great effort.

"Lauren?" His voice was little more than a croak. "Your head is bleeding. Are you . . . ?"

A sob caught in her throat. He was barely on his feet and yet he was worried about a cut on her cheek. "Joe . . ."

He collapsed before she could reach him. "Ryan!" she gasped, stumbling to Joe's side.

"Call 911, Lauren. Get an ambulance and the cops up here. Then see if you can stop Joe's bleeding while I make sure these two don't go anywhere. *Hurry,* Lauren!" he snapped when she hesitated at Joe's side, reluctant to leave him even for that long.

Forcing her limbs to cooperate, she threw herself toward the phone, praying incoherently in broken whispers. "Oh, please. Joe, *please . . .*"

There weren't many people in the hospital waiting room in the middle of the night. Lauren sat on a hard vinyl bench, twisting her hands in the hem of the sweatshirt she'd hastily thrown on with a pair of jeans as soon as the emergency medical team had arrived at the cabin for Joe. She hadn't even bothered to brush her hair; it tumbled wildly around her face and shoulders, half covering the neat white bandage a doctor had smoothed over the cut on the side of her face.

Her cheek still throbbed from the force of the blow she'd taken, but she ignored the discomfort, all her concentration focused on Joe, wondering what was happening to him, whether the ambulance had reached him in time. Pale and shaken out of his usual high spirits, Ryan paced the waiting room, his hands buried in the pockets of his jeans, his own hair tumbled over his forehead. He looked so much like Joe that Lauren's heart squeezed every time she looked at him. "Ryan, sit down," she said, patting the bench beside her. "You must be exhausted."

"I don't know how long I can sit still," he muttered, though he perched on the edge of the bench, his body held stiffly. "Damn, what's taking them so long?"

"I wish I knew," she whispered, staring futilely at the doorway of the waiting room.

Ryan reached over to take her icy hand in his bigger, warmer one. "He'll be okay, Lauren. I'm sure he will."

She wished he sounded more convinced. She knew he was as frightened as she was. She closed her fingers around his. "I know he will."

Ryan ran a hand through his hair, tousling it even more. "Now I know how Joe must have felt when I was hurt two years ago. When I was the one fighting for my life in a hospital bed."

"He was very worried about you. He's told me a little about it."

"Has he? He and I don't talk about it much."

"I know he took care of you while you recovered from your injuries."

"Yeah. He took care of me. He nagged me and goaded me into following the therapists' instructions, even when I didn't want to. He made me do all the exercises, bullied me into believing in myself even when my confidence was shaken. I don't know what I'd have done without him."

Lauren heard the love in Ryan's voice, and recognized it because she, too, loved the man they were discussing. She knew that whatever happened, she would love him for the rest of her life.

A doctor who'd first talked to them when Joe had been brought in entered the waiting room, bringing both Lauren and Ryan to their feet. "He's out of surgery," the doctor told them, his ebony face looking tired, his standard green scrubs spotted with blood.

Joe's blood, Lauren thought anxiously. "How is he?" she asked through lips so stiff she could hardly move them.

"He lost a lot of blood, but he was fortunate. The bullet passed cleanly through his shoulder. Tore some muscle and some ligaments, but no major damage. He'll need some therapy to regain full use of that arm, but he'll be back in top form before long. He's a lucky man."

Lauren's knees buckled. Ryan supported her with an arm around her waist. She felt the tremor run through him and knew he shared her staggering relief. "Thank God," he murmured.

Lauren wiped at her streaming eyes with a shaky hand. "When can we see him?"

"It'll be a while. You're both wiped out. Maybe you'd like to get some rest first, come back in the morning. He'll be pretty well out of it for the next few hours, anyway," the doctor suggested kindly.

"No." Lauren and Ryan spoke in near-perfect unison.

His mouth twisting wryly, Ryan added, "We'll wait until we've seen him."

The doctor nodded, apparently accustomed to the insistence. "You'll be notified when you can go in."

"Thank you," Lauren whispered in heartfelt gratitude.

Ryan warmly pumped the other man's hand. "I don't know how to repay you for saving my brother's life."

The doctor's dark face lit with a friendly smile. "Someone will be getting my bill. I'll be well paid."

"You won't hear any of us complaining," Ryan assured him, his own characteristic smile slowly returning to his eyes.

The moment they were alone again, Ryan turned and pulled Lauren into his arms, giving her a hug so tight it compressed her rib cage. She didn't complain, but hugged him back just as enthusiastically. "He's going to be okay, Lauren," Ryan said jubilantly.

"I know," she whispered through her tears. "I know, Ryan."

Something told her her silent prayer of gratitude was being fervently echoed by Ryan.

They found some vending machines in a deserted hospital canteen on the floor where Joe was being settled. The coffee was barely drinkable, but they downed two heavily sweetened cups apiece, needing the jolt of caffeine and sugar after the exhausting trauma of the past hours.

"What time is it?" Lauren asked after draining her second cup and shuddering at the bitter taste.

Ryan glanced at his watch. "After 2:00 a.m." He thought a moment, then suddenly looked up. "It's Joe's birthday!" he said, as though the thought had just occurred to him.

Startled, Lauren blinked. "It is?"

Ryan nodded. "Yeah. He's thirty."

"But...?" Puzzled by his phrasing, she cocked her head in curiosity. "It's your birthday, too, isn't it?"

His smile made him look more like himself than he had since Joe had been shot. "No. Mine's tomorrow."

"How...?"

"Joe was born at 11:55 p.m. on a Thursday. I was born at 12:05 a.m. Friday. Separate birthdays."

She laughed weakly and shook her head. "Trust the two of you to be so unique, even for identical twins."

"Our mother got a real kick out of it, especially when little Lindsay was born on a Sunday. Seven kids, seven different days of the week. One of the few things I remember about her is hearing her quote that little poem while she rocked the baby to sleep. You know, 'Monday's child is fair of face' and so on.''

"I know it," Lauren agreed. "As a matter of fact, I'm a Friday's child, myself."

"Loving and giving," Ryan quoted. "It suits you."

"It suits you, too," she answered with a gentle smile, thinking of his love for his brother. And then her smile faded. "So Joe is Thursday's child."

Ryan nodded gravely. "'Thursday's child has far to go.' That, too, seems appropriate."

Joe certainly seemed to have "far to go" in finding happiness in his life, Lauren mused sadly. If only...

But, no. No more regrets tonight, she told herself firmly. Tonight, she was just going to be grateful that Joe was alive.

She'd come so very close to losing him forever.

Joe was groggy, barely conscious when Lauren and Ryan were finally allowed to see him. He was still deathly pale, swathed in bandages, connected to IVs and monitors, but he was alive and out of danger. Lauren thought he looked absolutely beautiful.

She bent over him, her face close to his. "Joe? Can you hear me?"

He stirred against the pillow, moaning a bit as he forced his eyelids open. "Lauren?"

She swallowed hard. "Yes. How do you feel?"

"Like hell. How about you? How's your head?"

"I'm fine. You saved my life, Joe."

"I damned near got you killed," he muttered harshly. "If I'd been more careful—"

"You took a bullet trying to protect me," she interrupted firmly. "And then you forced yourself off that floor and rescued me when that man held a gun to my head. I refuse to hear any criticism of your actions—from you or anyone else. Is that clear?"

"I wouldn't argue with her, Joe," Ryan said, his voice holding a smile. "She sounds pretty fierce."

"She can be," Joe murmured. "How you doing, Ry?"

"Okay. No injuries this time."

"That's a refreshing change." Joe's voice had gotten lower, his eyelids heavier. "I'm ... uh ..."

"You need your rest," Lauren finished for him. She smoothed a damp lock of hair away from his forehead. "Go to sleep, Joe. We'll be back in the morning."

"Yeah." His eyes closed briefly, and then he forced them back open. "Ryan?"

"Yeah, Joe?"

"Take care of her."

"I will."

Lauren brushed her mouth over Joe's. "Good night, Joe."

His eyes were closed again. "'Night," he mumbled, already mostly asleep.

She blinked back tears and drew a shaky breath. "I love you," she whispered. And then she straightened and turned back to Ryan, her chin held high. "I'm ready to go now."

He touched his brother's arm, as if to reassure himself that Joe really was all right, and then he nodded brusquely. "Okay. Let's go."

Lauren let Ryan go into Joe's room first the next day. She waited outside in the hallway, giving the brothers a few minutes of privacy. She was torn between impatience to see Joe again and an odd nervousness about doing so. She smoothed her freshly washed hair with one hand, moistening her carefully glossed lips as she did so. She knew she looked much different now than she had when she'd left the hospital some ten hours earlier. She'd had some sleep and a shower, had combed her hair and made up her newly bruised face, and she was wearing a cream silk blouse and beige linen slacks that she knew were flattering.

She didn't know why it had seemed so important to look her best today, nor why she was so anxious about the impending visit with Joe. Maybe because she sensed that whatever they said now would determine their entire future together—or apart.

Ryan gave her a rueful grimace when he came out of Joe's room. "He's not exactly in a cheery mood," he cautioned her. "He's being a real grouch, to be honest."

She'd half expected that. She'd never thought Joe would be a gracious, uncomplaining patient. "Thanks for warning me."

He tossed her a bracing, thumbs-up gesture. "Good luck. I'm going to get some more of that delightful coffee they serve here."

"Then *you're* the one who should be wished luck," she replied, stalling for just another moment before going into Joe's room.

"You may be right. If I survive, I'll be back in a little while." He patted her shoulder as he passed her on his way down the hallway. Lauren realized he was trying to encourage her. Could he see how nervous she was? Did he understand?

Taking a deep breath, she clutched the package in her hand a bit more tightly and pushed open the swinging door to Joe's room.

He was lying against the pillows, his bare chest still swathed in bandages, his left arm still strapped down with an IV needle. He was scowling, as she'd expected, but the color had come back to his face since she'd last seen him.

She breathed a sigh of relief at the visible improvement in his condition, if not his mood. "How are you feeling?" she asked him, slowly approaching the bed.

He gave her a brooding look. "How do you think I feel?"

"I'm sure I can guess." She stood beside the bed, her hands clasped loosely in front of her. "The doctors said you're going to be fine. I'm so glad."

"It's just a scratch," he said gruffly, and not quite accurately. She knew he didn't want her to fuss over him, that it embarrassed him to be an invalid, no matter how temporarily. She bit back the words of sympathy she wanted to offer.

Before she could think of anything else to say, he nodded toward the bandage on her face. "Does it hurt?"

"Not at all," she fibbed. "I've got some fetching new bruises, though," she added wryly, thinking of the colorful marks on the arm her assailant had handled so roughly. "I seem to attract them lately."

Joe didn't smile. "You're sure you're okay?"

"I'm fine. Really."

"Your father will probably blame me for every bruise."

"My father is very grateful to you for saving my life. Several times," she answered firmly. "He doesn't blame you for anything. At the moment, he's too busy blaming himself for leading those jerks to us."

"Ryan told me about it. Said your father's secretary broke into his locked desk and found the address he'd written down. That she managed to smuggle the information out before she was caught."

"My father really trusted her," Lauren said sadly. "She'd been with him over five years. She always seemed like a very nice woman to me, too. Neither of us knew she had a son in serious financial trouble, a son who'd gotten mixed up with the Chosen Ones during the past year. She said she'd been assured that I wouldn't be hurt, but they made threats against her son if she wouldn't help them find me."

"I hope they lock her up."

"She was frightened, Joe. He's her only son."

Joe wasn't moved. "And you're Caldwell's only daughter. You almost died in Arkansas and you could have been killed last night with all those wild shots ricocheting around. She doesn't deserve your sympathy. Or your father's."

"She won't get any from him," Lauren said with a sigh. "Dad fired her, of course, and fully intends to press charges. He'll never forgive her for betraying him."

"Good." He glanced at her, still standing so stiffly beside his bed, and motioned impatiently toward the chair behind her. "Sit down."

Not exactly a gracious invitation, but Lauren didn't chide him for his tone as she drew the chair nearer. Before she sat, she handed him the package she'd carried in. "This is for you. Happy birthday, Joe."

He looked down at the tissue-wrapped, soft package in his hands. "How did you know it was my birthday?"

"Ryan told me, of course. Aren't you going to open it?"

"You didn't have to get me anything."

"Just open it before you start thanking me."

Though he seemed oddly reluctant to do so, he peeled away the tissue, holding the package with his strapped-down left hand while he unwrapped with his right. He recognized the contents immediately. "It's the sweater you were knitting," he said, studying the pale blue knitted garment.

"Yes. It should fit you. Of course, it will be too warm for you to wear it now, but you can save it until the weather turns cool again. That particular winter sweater is the only pattern I know by heart," she explained with a touch of apology.

"I didn't know you were making this for me."

"I know. I wanted to surprise you."

"It's beautiful, Lauren. Thank you."

She relaxed a bit in the uncomfortable chair. "You're welcome."

He looked at the sweater for several more long, silent moments, apparently trying to think of something else to say. She rather regretted that when he spoke, it was only to return to the subject of the second attempted kidnapping, as though he was reminding himself of who she was and why she was here, she thought in faint resentment. "Ryan said the two guys who broke in on us last night are in custody, and the Chicago cops think they've rounded up all the ones responsible for that last attempt on your father."

Lauren nodded reluctantly. "That's what we were told. With Dad's secretary under arrest, as well, there aren't many members of the gang free to cause any trouble."

"I won't feel completely comfortable about your safety until Bullock is convicted."

"I won't be taking any foolish risks," she promised.

He looked at her. "What are you going to do now?"

Her fingers tightened in her lap. "What do you mean?"

"You know damned well what I mean. Where are you going to stay? Obviously I can't watch out for you during the next few days."

"Ryan's still on the payroll," she reminded him. "I still have a bodyguard."

Joe's expression grew even more forbidding, if possible. "Where will you be staying? Obviously you can't stay at the cabin, since that location is known to them now."

"I'm tired of being shuffled among strange places," she answered. "If I can't stay here, I might as well go home."

"To your apartment? No way." He hadn't even hesitated before rejecting the suggestion.

She didn't point out that the decision wasn't his to make. "I really do think it's over, Joe. Dad promised the trial will only take a few more days. Any of Bullock's followers who haven't already been arrested have to realize the futility of trying to use me to influence the outcome of the trial. It was just those two who broke in last night—they were determined to get to me, however uselessly. They're crazy."

"I still don't like the thought of you going back to your apartment. Not even with Ryan there to watch out for you. Apartments are too easily accessible. Too many other tenants around to accidentally mess things up."

"My father wants me to spend the next couple of weeks at his house," she admitted. "The security there is very tight—fences and cameras and patrol dogs, the works—and there's plenty of room for me and a whole team of bodyguards if I want them."

His expression unchanging, Joe nodded. "That would probably be best. Is that what you're going to do?"

She tried desperately to read his expression. He looked so hard, so distant—so unlike the man who'd made such sweet, tender love to her only hours before. "What I'd really like to do," she said quietly, "is to stay here in Colorado. With you."

His eyelids dropped, hiding his eyes from her. "I'm told I'll be laid up here for several more days."

"I could stay at the cabin. Visit you here every day. With Ryan around, I'd be perfectly safe."

He hesitated so long she began to hope he'd agree. Her hopes were dashed when he slowly shook his head. "It's probably better if you leave now. As you can see, I'm going to be fine. There's really no need for you to hang around here any longer."

She forced her voice past the sudden lump in her throat. "I had hoped you'd want me to stay."

"Lauren, I thought we'd made this clear from the beginning. I was your bodyguard. It was always temporary. Now that I'm off the case, it's over."

The words hit her like a slap. It didn't help at all that Joe had seemed to have some difficulty saying them. "Is that all you can say?" she whispered. "That it's over?"

A muscle twitched in his jaw. It was the only part of him that moved. "What else *can* I say? It's best for us to end it now, before it goes any further. Before anyone gets hurt any worse."

A tremor of anger ran through her, drawing her clenched fingers into fists. "You're always saying that," she accused him heatedly. "Always deciding what's 'best' for everyone. You never stop to ask what anyone else wants. Not Ryan. Not your other brothers and sisters. Not me. Only what's easiest for you."

"I suppose I am a selfish bastard," he agreed evenly, though a faint white line had become just visible around his mouth. "You're much better off without me."

"Maybe I don't think so."

"Lauren, don't make this any harder for either of us."

"I'm not going to beg, if that's what you're worried about," she said stiffly, remaining pride lifting her chin. "I can't make you love me, Joe. I had hoped you'd learn to do that on your own."

He didn't answer, but kept his gaze trained darkly on the sweater clenched tightly in his hand.

She sighed, silently, wearily conceding defeat. She'd tried, and she'd lost. She could survive this, she told herself dully. She'd always survived before.

"What are you going to do now?" she asked, hearing the heaviness of her voice, unable to do anything about it. "After you get out of the hospital, I mean."

"I'll stay at the cabin awhile, get my strength back, do whatever exercises I have to do to get my shoulder back in shape. And then I'll get back into the old routine. Take another assignment. Get on with my life."

She nodded. "And your family? Have you reconsidered contacting them?"

"No. I have no interest in getting entangled in those sorts of ties."

She felt her heart break with the words. He really had made up his mind, she thought. About his family—and about her. He was rejecting all of them.

"I suppose I might as well go now," she murmured, slowly rising from the chair. "There doesn't seem to be any reason for me to linger here."

He hesitated only a moment before nodding. "I think I'll get some rest. Tell Ryan to give me a call when you've made your plans. If you're going back to Chicago, I want him to go with you. I'd rather he'd be with you—at least until you're safely settled into your father's house—than hanging around here with me."

"I believe that's up to Ryan," Lauren said coolly. Joe really wasn't the authority over everyone, despite what he seemed to believe, she told herself in silent defiance.

He only nodded, as though Ryan's cooperation was already guaranteed.

It was harder than she could have even imagined to make herself leave Joe's room. She stepped closer to the bed, taking her courage in both hands as she leaned over to brush her lips across his. "Goodbye, Joe. Take care of yourself," she whispered against his mouth.

His lips held hers for a moment, the kiss holding a hint of the passion they'd shared before. Joe was the first to draw back. "Goodbye, Lauren."

She didn't pause again until she'd reached the door. His image wavered through a thin film of tears when she looked back at him. "I love you," she said. "I don't think you've heard those words nearly enough in your life."

His eyes were haunted when he answered. "Maybe if I'd heard them earlier, when I was younger..." he murmured. "But it's too late now. I can't change what I've become—and you deserve a hell of a lot more."

"I don't agree with you," she said. "You're everything I've ever wanted. If you... if you change your mind about us, you know where to find me."

His expression had closed again. "Goodbye, Lauren."

She swallowed a sob and left the room before she could make even more of a pathetic fool of herself.

It was over, she thought as the door swooshed closed behind her. All over.

She'd carry the scars of the past few weeks for the rest of her life. Not the physical scars—those would heal soon enough. It was her heart that would never fully recover.

Chapter Fifteen

Joe had been reading for more than an hour and he still hadn't finished a chapter of the newest bestselling mystery thriller he'd started the day before. Realizing that he was reading the same page for the third time, he muttered a curse and slammed the book shut.

Across the room, Ryan looked up from his own book. "Problem?"

"Tired of sitting around. Why don't we go into town, have a few drinks at Charley's? Seems like we've been stuck in this cabin for months."

"You've only been out of the hospital three weeks. The doctors told you to take it slow until you get all your strength back."

"I've been taking it slow. And I'm tired of it. You going to Charley's with me or am I going alone?"

"I'll go. One of us has to drive home. The mood you're in, you're liable to drink too much then try to drive yourself."

"I don't drive drunk. You know that."

"Right. But I'm still going. And I'm driving."

"You can be a real pain sometimes, Ryan."

Ryan didn't look particularly perturbed by the accusation. "So I've been told."

Joe spun impatiently toward his bedroom. "I'm going to change my shirt. We'll leave in ten minutes."

"Yes, boss man."

Joe didn't even bother to respond to the taunt.

He was buttoning his clean shirt when the phone rang. It stopped before he could reach for the extension on his nightstand. Ryan must have answered it. With little enthusiasm, Joe ran a comb through his hair before leaving his bedroom, tucking his wallet into his back pocket as he headed for the living room.

Ryan was just hanging up the phone. "That was Miller," he said. "Wanted to check on you."

"Yeah? What'd you tell him?"

"The truth. That your arm is getting better and your mood is getting lousier."

Joe shrugged, the movement pulling uncomfortably at the still-tender wound. "Maybe he'll put me back to work to rescue you from any further hassle from me."

"You know he's not putting you back to work until you've got clearance from the doctor. And that's going to be at least another month."

"Damn."

"Hey, it took me a year. Count your blessings."

Joe grumbled an answer, unable to think of any blessings at the moment. His life was in one hell of a mess—and he was supposed to be thankful? Not likely.

"Miller mentioned some news from Chicago," Ryan remarked, his attention seemingly focused on removing a spot of lint from his dark jeans. "Said Bullock was convicted a few days ago. There hasn't been any further trouble from what few of his followers remain at large. Looks like Lauren and her father should be able to relax their security now."

The sound of Lauren's name was like a blow to Joe's chest. He'd tried so damned hard not to think of her during the past few weeks. He'd failed miserably, of course. She was just about all he *had* thought about, particularly during the long, near-sleepless nights that had passed since Ryan had escorted her back to Chicago. "I'm sure they're relieved," he said, trying to sound only idly interested.

He should have known Ryan wouldn't let it go at that. "You are such an idiot—and you're a lousy actor, too," Ryan complained. "I never realized what a stupid jerk my own brother was—and to think I share your genes. It's a daunting thought, I can tell you."

"Don't start with me again, Ry. I mean it."

"Yeah, sure. I'm supposed to go on pretending everything's just fine, right? Acting like I don't know you're tearing yourself apart over her."

"Don't, Ryan."

In an uncharacteristic display of temper, Ryan slammed the book he'd been holding down on the coffee table, knocking a television remote control to the floor with a clatter. "Well, *damn it,* Joe, what do you expect from me? How long do you think I can stand to watch you like this?"

"I don't—"

"She *loves* you, damn it. It nearly killed her when you were shot in front of her eyes. And you love her. Don't even try to tell me you don't, or I'm liable to take your hard head off. So why the hell are you here while she's in Chicago, will you just tell me that?"

"And just what the hell am I supposed to offer her here?" Joe exploded, his own raw temper igniting. "This luxurious mansion?" he asked sarcastically, swinging a hand to indicate their simple, rustic surroundings. "You expect me to take her away from her home and her career to sit here and wait patiently for me to come back from assignments to God knows where?

"Or maybe you think I should go to her in Chicago," he went on flatly. "Let her and her rich father support me because I'm not qualified for anything but maybe working as a security guard at her apartment building."

"That's the biggest crock of—"

Joe cut into Ryan's disgusted exclamation. "It wouldn't work, Ryan. I don't know how to live that straight, nine-to-five life. And you know as well as I do that I sure as hell don't know anything about normal family life. She wants marriage and kids and everything that goes with it. I haven't been a part of a real family since I was five years old—and to say our early family life was dysfunctional is rather an understatement, wouldn't you agree?"

"Maybe," Ryan said evenly, speaking more quietly now. "But you have been a member of a family, Joe. You know all about caring and loyalty and being there when you're needed. You've done all that for me. You could do it for Lauren, for the kids the two of you could have together. You'd be pretty damned terrific at it, actually. If you can't see that, then you're even more blind than I thought."

His own temper evaporating, Joe wearily shook his head. "You don't understand."

"No. I don't understand. If I've ever felt the way you feel about Lauren—well, I've forgotten. I only know that she's a very special woman and what she offered you was a once-in-a-lifetime opportunity for you. Are you really going to let her slip away this easily, Joe? Do you really want some other guy to recognize all she has to offer and take advantage of it for himself?''

The thought of Lauren with another man made Joe want to put his fist through a wall—preferably one made of concrete. He turned away before Ryan could see what the image did to him.

"You've always tried to tell me what was best for me, and now I'm going to do the same for you. Lauren is best for you, Joe. She's the very best thing that's ever happened to you. Don't let her get away."

A long silence followed Ryan's heartfelt advice. Joe finally broke it with a gusty exhale. "I'll think about it," he said. "That's all I can promise."

"It's a start," Ryan approved. "A damned good start. Now why don't we go on over to Charley's? I think it would do us both a lot of good to get out of here for a few hours."

Marcus Caldwell had always taken great pride in the prize-winning rose garden his late wife had planted behind his house. He'd employed two full-time gardeners just to take care of it since his wife's death so many years ago. Lauren wandered down the elegantly curved paths without even being aware of the lush, fragrant beauty surrounding her, hardly even aware when a thorn scratched her hand as she brushed past one particularly heavy-laden bush.

The Saturday afternoon June sun spilled over her, warming her skin through the thin white cotton of her sleeveless dress. She hadn't come outside to admire the roses, or to enjoy the perfect weather. She'd come out to be alone, to try to find some sort of enthusiasm for going on with the rest of her life.

The trial was over. Everyone agreed it would be safe to go back to her apartment now. Under ordinary conditions, the security measures employed by her upscale apartment building were perfectly sufficient. Lauren should be perfectly safe there now. She just hadn't had the desire yet to move back home.

Her father's accountant had taken excellent care of her business during the time she'd been away. Lauren had been able to smoothly take over again upon her return, managing her accounts from her father's house for the duration, explaining to her clients that she was still recuperating from her "accident," but expected to be back in her offices within the month. Everyone had been remarkably patient and cooperative. There had been no complaints at all, as far as she knew.

Her friends were delighted to have her back. She'd been inundated with invitations—parties, dinners, lunches. She'd politely refused them all, men and women, having had no interest in socializing for now. She couldn't even imagine dating again, couldn't picture herself being intimate with any man other than Joe. The thought of even kissing another man left her cold, empty. Miserable.

Even her father was starting to worry about her, gruffly pushing her to get on with her life, assuming she was still getting over the trauma of being targeted twice for kidnapping. He'd asked about Joe, but she'd shrugged off his questions. She believed she'd been successful in convincing him that there had been nothing serious between her and the bodyguard Marcus had provided her. It was a measure of how little Marcus knew her that he'd accepted those lies without further question.

Her wounds had all healed, the final bruises faded. There would be no lasting physical damage from her ordeal.

Everything was going along just fine.

And Lauren was so unhappy that she had to make a massive effort to drag herself out of bed each morning, so depressed, it was all she could do to get through each day.

She missed him. She'd never imagined missing anyone as deeply, as desperately, as she missed Joe.

It didn't matter that she'd told herself over and again that she'd only known him a few weeks, that it had been a month since she'd seen him. It didn't matter that he'd sent her away, rejected the love she'd all but begged him to accept. She still loved him, and she missed him. She thought it quite likely that she always would.

He'd cared for her, in his way. She reminded herself of that each time she thought she couldn't bear the pain any longer, and it had helped. A little. If only his feelings for her had been strong enough to overcome a lifetime of wariness and mistrust. If only...

She couldn't bear to think of him being alone for the rest of his life. Joe had so much love to offer, needed love so badly. But would he ever allow himself to care for anyone other than his twin? Would he ever find a woman he could trust with his heart? Though it devastated her to even think of him with another woman, she hoped for his sake that he would someday find someone. Before it was too late.

She loved him too much to wish anything but the best for him, even after he'd hurt her as badly as he had.

A sound from behind her made her gasp and jump. As she turned to investigate, she chided herself for still being so skittish, even though she'd been assured that she was safe now. Would she spend the rest of her life dodging shadows? Was she really going to let those bastards do that to her?

He stood on the path behind her, his hands in the pockets of his snug-fitting jeans as he watched her with a wary expression. For a moment she was so stunned she wasn't even sure which one he was. Ryan, impulsively dropping by to check on her? Or—

"Joe," she whispered, her heart recognizing him even before her eyes did.

"Hello, Lauren."

It was Joe's voice. Deep, rough, wonderful. Feeling her knees go weak in response, she groped for support. Then winced in pain when her hand closed over a branch full of thorns. "Ouch!"

He stepped quickly forward, reaching for her hand. "Let me see."

They both looked down at the drops of scarlet decorating her palm. One wicked thorn still pierced her skin; Joe gently removed it, tossing it aside as he looked for more.

Lauren made a sound of self-disgust and shook her head. "Why is it that I always seem to be bruised or bleeding when you find me?"

Still cradling her hand in his own, he looked up at her. "Maybe I'm bad luck for you."

"No," she whispered, meeting his gaze with her own, unable to hide any of her tumultuous feelings at seeing him again. "I don't think that's it, at all."

He lifted her hand to his mouth and pressed a warm, lingering kiss in her punctured palm. She trembled, her breath catching in her throat.

He kept her hand in his right one when he lowered their arms. "You've lost weight," he said. "You didn't need to."

"I haven't been very hungry lately." She tried without much success to read his expression. "How are you? Your shoulder?"

"Almost completely healed," he assured her, raising his left arm and rotating it to prove his point. "See?"

She couldn't stand it any longer. The words burst out of her. "Joe, why are you here?"

His left arm fell to his side, though he kept her right hand tight in his. "Before I answer that, maybe you'd better tell me whether you're glad to see me."

"Glad?" she repeated incredulously, her voice thick. "I've wanted to see you so badly. I've missed you so much. How can you even ask if I'm glad to see you?"

"Lauren," he murmured, cupping her cheek in his free hand. "God, I've missed you."

And then he kissed her, and the deep, raw hunger of the embrace rocked her all the way down to her toes. She wrapped an arm around his neck and pulled him more tightly to her, not at all sure she'd ever be able to let him go now that she held him again.

The need for oxygen finally made him draw back with a gasp. He held her tightly in his arms as he struggled to control his breathing, his lean cheek pressed to her hair. Her eyes closed, Lauren clung to him. It hurt, she realized, to hope this much. But not as badly as it had hurt to have her hopes dashed before.

She somehow found the courage to tilt her head back to look up at him. "Please tell me you aren't going to send me away again."

His crooked smile wasn't quite steady. "How could I send you away? This is your father's house, remember?"

She didn't return the smile, refusing to be diverted by his attempt at teasing her. "You know what I mean. Why are you here, Joe? Why have you found me this time?"

He gazed down at her, his light blue eyes warmer than she'd ever seen them. "I thought it was best for you to send you away," he murmured. "I thought I'd learn to live without you. Maybe I was right about you, but I was wrong about me. I can't live without you, Lauren. I don't want to try."

"You weren't right about me," she told him sternly, gripping his pale blue cotton shirt in both hands, ignoring the resulting small bloodstains that dotted the fabric. "It was cruel of you to send me away. You broke my heart, damn it! And I don't want to live without you, either."

"I don't have a thing to offer you, Lauren. I never went to college, I only have a high school equivalency certificate. My job isn't exactly conducive to stable family life, but I don't know anything else. I've got enough money put aside to last for a while, but not indefinitely, and I'll be damned if I'll let you or your father support us. But if you'll have me—"

"I'll have you," she answered promptly, needing no time to think. "I don't care what you do, or where we live, or how. I love you, Joe. I just want to be with you."

He drew a deep, ragged breath. "I don't deserve you," he muttered, his eyes hungry on her face. "But I love you. I never thought I'd love anyone like this, but I do. And I promise I'll spend the rest of my life trying to be worthy of you."

Her eyes flooded. "You really don't know how special you are, do you?" she whispered. "How lucky I am to be loved by a man like you. If it takes that long, I'll spend the rest of my life convincing you."

He lowered his mouth to hers. Hard. It was a very long time before either of them could speak again.

"Damn," Joe said when at last they reluctantly drew apart. "I'd love to carry you to the nearest bed, but something tells me your father wouldn't approve. I guess we'd better go in and face him."

"My—?" Lauren suddenly realized exactly where they were. She gasped and looked toward the house, wondering if she saw a tall, heavy form standing in one of the many gleaming windows. "He's inside. How did you know I was out here? How did you get onto the estate?"

"Your father let me in, and he told me where to find you." Joe's mouth twisted into a wry smile. "He said he'd been expecting me to show up for the past three weeks. Seemed resigned to it. And he told me if I hurt you again, he was going to personally rip my heart out. Through my throat, I think he said."

Lauren was stunned. "My father *knew?* About us?"

"You didn't tell him?"

"No. I told him we were just, um, friends."

"I don't think he bought it."

"Apparently not." Maybe her father knew her better than she'd given him credit, she thought, rather pleased with the idea.

"You know, he's not really all that bad, after all," Joe offered magnanimously. "I think we'll manage to get along—as long as he keeps his nose out of our business, of course."

Lauren smiled broadly and hugged him. "Thank you, Joe. It won't always be easy, but I'm glad you're willing to try to get along with him. He *is* my father."

His hands lingered at her hips when the hug ended. She recognized the look in his eyes, and her pulse leapt in response. "Will you be staying here tonight?" he asked, his voice just a bit husky.

"I think I'd like to spend tonight at my own apartment," she answered with a meaningful smile. "Maybe you'd like to see it?"

"I'd love to see it," he assured her fervently. "Just as long as it's got a bed."

"It's got a bed. Plenty big enough for the both of us."

He took her hand and tugged her toward the house. "Then what are we waiting for? Let's go talk to your father and get the hell out of here."

Laughing, she hurried to keep up with him, as eager as Joe was to be alone again.

Lauren's apartment was dark and quiet, a private, intimate setting for the two lovers entwined in her big canopy bed. She lay at Joe's side, her hand on his damp, bare, scarred chest, his heart still racing beneath her fingers. Her own breathing was ragged, but slowly quieting, her body heavy and sated from their lovemaking.

"Joe?" she said when she was sure she could speak coherently again.

"Mmm?"

"I really would like to meet them."

He went still. "Damn it, Lauren."

She'd known he wouldn't need clarification. "They're your family, Joe. They're a part of you, part of your past. I want to see them. I think you do, too, if you'd just be honest with me—and with yourself."

"Lauren, I don't know—"

"Ryan wants to see them, too. He didn't say, because he didn't want to upset you, but I could see it in his eyes. He's curious."

"Ryan's always curious."

"I know, but this is different. This is his family."

Joe was still for so long she was beginning to wonder if he was going to answer her at all. Finally he sighed gustily and said, "I'll think about it, okay? No promises, but I'll think about it."

"Thank you. I really believe it's important. I think it will haunt both of us—all three of us—until you do something about it."

"I still don't know what you hope to accomplish with this. These people are strangers. After so many years, we couldn't possibly have anything in common, won't have any of those cozy, familial feelings you seem to expect."

"I don't expect you to fall into their arms, Joe," she said rather acerbically. "I just think you need to settle your past before we embark on our future. Doesn't that make sense?"

He sighed again, shook his head against the pillows and muttered, "I'll think about it. Just don't push."

"I won't push," she promised, and crossed her fingers beneath the sheets.

"You are going to marry me, aren't you?"

It was the first time he'd mentioned the M word. Lauren swallowed hard, then managed to say fairly evenly, "I don't know."

His arm jerked convulsively around her. "What the hell do you mean, you don't know? Why the hell don't you know?"

She stifled a smile at his typically impatient outburst. "How am I supposed to marry you when I don't even know your full name?" she asked pointedly.

"Oh." He cleared his throat. "Walker," he muttered after a brief pause. "I was christened Joseph Brian Walker."

"Joseph Brian Walker," she repeated, savoring the syllables. "And Ryan?"

"Robert Ryan. He always liked his middle name best."

"So do I," she said after thinking about it a moment.

"Well?" Joe demanded aggressively.

"Yes, Joseph Brian Walker. I would be happy and honored to marry you. Whenever and wherever you like."

"Soon," he said, twisting to loom over her in the bed, his mouth hovering a breath away from hers. "Very soon."

"Right now if we could," she murmured, wrapping her arms around his neck.

He kissed her deeply, approvingly, letting her know that now couldn't be soon enough, as far as he was concerned.

They were going to be married, she thought, happiness bubbling wildly inside her. Joe would be her husband, Ryan her beloved brother-in-law. And then they'd meet the other brothers and sisters. She knew Joe wouldn't be able to resist her requests for long.

It would be a happy experience for him, she thought with irrepressible optimism. For all of them. They would be the family she'd long craved and Joe had so desperately needed, whether he'd admitted it or not.

Everything was different now that Joseph Brian Walker had finally learned to open his heart again to love.

He'd come a very long way since he'd pulled her out of that flooding stream, she thought contentedly, arching into his eager hands. A very long way, indeed.

YOU'LL BE INTRIGUED BY OUR NEW SERIES

Intrigue, the new series from Silhouette, features romantic tales of danger and suspense.

The intriguing plots will keep you turning page after page as the gripping stories reveal mystery, murder and even a touch of the supernatural.

4 titles every month, priced at £1.95 each, from July 1994.

Available from WH Smith, John Menzies, Volume One, Forbuoys, Martins, Woolworths, Tesco, Asda, Safeway and other paperback stockists. Also available from Silhouette Reader Service, FREEPOST, PO Box 236, Croydon, Surrey CR9 9EL. (UK Postage & Packing free)

THREE STEAMING HOT LOVE STORIES FOR SUMMER FROM SILHOUETTE

When the entire South-East of the United States is suddenly without power, passions ignite as the temperature soars.

SILHOUETTE

Available from July 1994   Price: £3.99

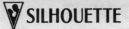

▼ SILHOUETTE

⟩ SPECIAL EDITION ⟨

COMING NEXT MONTH

SALLY JANE GOT MARRIED Celeste Hamilton

That Special Woman!

Sally Jane Haskins was the local scarlet woman. So what did the town's most eligible newcomer see in her? Maybe he didn't believe the local gossip. Maybe he *did*...

HE'S MY SOLDIER BOY Lisa Jackson

Mavericks

Dark, sexy and dangerous, Ben Powell had left Carlie Surrett with shattered dreams because he blamed her for the tragedy that followed their passion. Now he was back and his time in the army had not softened his attitude!

WHEN STARS COLLIDE Patricia Coughlin

Rachel Curtis had given up everything to protect her niece, but state prosecutor Mitch Dalton inadvertently threatened their safety. How did Rachel get rid of him when she really wanted him to stay?

MARRY ME KATE Tracy Sinclair

Hunter Warburton's son was running circles round his busy dad and Kate Merriweather found herself falling hard for both of them. But could she marry a man who didn't love her?

WITH BABY IN MIND Arlene James

How did a bad-boy bachelor transform himself into a family man? Parker persuaded his friend Kendra to marry him so that he would retain custody of his baby niece; but could he seduce his wife?

DENVER'S LADY Jennifer Mikels

Kelly Shelton was her own woman—until she met Denver Casey rodeo champion. Could she risk everything for a bittersweet spell as Denver's lady?

COMING NEXT MONTH FROM

▼ SILHOUETTE

Intrigue

*Danger, deception and desire—
new from Silhouette...*

NIGHT MOVES Nora Roberts
TIGER'S DEN Andrea Davidson
WHISTLEBLOWER Tess Gerritsen
MURDER BY THE BOOK Margaret St George

Desire

*Provocative, sensual love stories for the
woman of today*

WILD INNOCENCE Ann Major
YESTERDAY'S OUTLAW Raye Morgan
SEVEN YEAR ITCH Peggy Moreland
TWILIGHT MAN Karen Leabo
RICH GIRL, BAD BOY Audra Adams
BLACK LACE AND LINEN Susan Carroll

Sensation

*A thrilling mix of passion, adventure,
and drama*

MACKENZIE'S MISSION Linda Howard
EXILE'S END Rachel Lee
THE HELL-RAISER Dallas Schulze
THE LOVE OF DUGAN MAGEE Linda Turner

HEART  HEART

Win a year's supply of Silhouette Special Edition books ABSOLUTELY FREE?

Yes, you can win one whole year's supply of Silhouette Special Edition books. It's easy! Find a path through the maze, starting at the top left square and finishing at the bottom right. The symbols must follow the sequence above. You can move up, down, left, right and diagonally.

Please turn over for entry details

HEART  HEART

SEND YOUR ENTRY NOW!

The first five correct entries picked out of the bag after the closing date will each win one year's supply of Silhouette Special Edition books (six books every month for twelve months - worth over £85). What could be easier?

Don't forget to enter your name and address in the space below then put this page in an envelope and post it today (you don't need a stamp). Competition closes 31st December 1994.

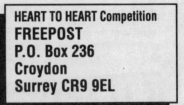

HEART TO HEART Competition
FREEPOST
P.O. Box 236
Croydon
Surrey CR9 9EL

Are you a Reader Service subscriber?   Yes ☐   No ☐

Ms/Mrs/Miss/Mr _____ COMSE

Address _____

_____

_____

Postcode _____

Signature _____